Don't Kiss Your Turtle Goodbye

Gerald Orr
with
Ann Tankersley

Illustrated by Tim Rickard

DOWN HOME

Down Home Press
Asheboro, NC 27203

To our friend and mentor,
Beth Martin,
who insisted we could and should
write this book together,
and to
Betsy Orr and L. C. Tankersley,
who said Beth was right.
We are forever grateful for their
editorial suggestions, encouragement,
love and laughter.

Ann Tankersley

Acknowledgements

My warmest thanks to office partners Dr. James T. Mullikin and Dr. Ronald J. Outlaw, and to staffers Stephanie Brown, Carol Crawford, Cindy Hood, Marcine Suttles, Dean Trammell, Zana Williams and Sue Youngblood, each of whom helped make this book possible, and also to colleagues the late Dr. Jodie Blackwell, Dr. Sam Kellett, Dr. Michael Oliver and Dr. Poag Reid, without whose inspiration, there would have been no book to write.

Gerald Orr, D.V.M.
June 7, 1995

Contents

Chapter 1

Squeals in the Night

Pigs are not my forte.

After I left home at fifteen, to be able to have a place to live and eat, I had to take care of 300 hogs. I had to feed them and wash down their pens. I hauled garbage from the Furman University dining hall and cooked it for them. I hammered many tons of dusty hog feed on hot summer days. Once I got into veterinary practice, I was determined to let my associates take care of the pigs. Pigs were out.

It was a good day for me when I joined in practice with Dr. Jim Mullikin, at the clinic where I now work. Our office is in Easley, South Carolina, in the Blue Ridge Mountain foothills, but our calls take us all over a beautiful country of rolling pasture lands, woods and mountains.

It's a good place to practice and a good place to live, a mostly rural place. You can sit on your porch on a clear night and count a million stars, while you listen to the tree frogs and peepers singing the oldest song on earth. Or you can drive to Greenville or Anderson, or even Atlanta, for a different sort of night-life.

Domestic farm animals and family pets account for most of our practice. We get calls to care for wild animals, too, and occasionally, a patient is exotic enough to send us back to the books. My own love is horses and other large animals. But whenever I can, I let my partners handle pig calls.

They like pigs.

On my first day at the clinic, Dr. Mullikin had to go out to Alice Farms and take blood samples from 200 sows. That was a fine, healthy herd, and they were tested every four months to be sure nothing was going wrong. It was a tough job. I didn't want to be obnoxious about it—at least not on the first day. So we went out there together.

To do this test, you first took a pair of tongs and caught the sow at the crest of her neck. Or you put a nose snare on her and tied her to a pole. But for a split second, anyway, you had to get her still and not let her thrash around—because you had to stick a five-inch needle through her neck, into the anterior vena cava, and draw blood. It was one of those things where you either did it right, or you had a lot of bacon.

We and the pigs lived through that one. But when we walked back in the office, I said, "Jim, I'll go in practice with you, if you do the hogs and give me anything else that walks through that door." That was it for pigs. Absolutely.

Well, I was on call one night. Way late in the night, I'd just cut off the TV and turned out the light. And the phone rang. I sighed, picked it up, and a voice rattled in my ear: "Doc, my sow has been tryin' to have her little pigs all day long. She had two this morning, but ain't nothin' happened since."

It's an old story. Some folks will mess around all day with an ailing animal, thinking—hoping—that it'll get better. Then they realize midnight's coming on; that's when they lose it. They don't want to be left alone in the dark with an animal they think is going to die.

It was my partners' night to relax, and mine to work. This guy named Sam was worried about his sow. He needed a vet, and that was me. I had no choice. Push had come to shove, as we say in the birthing business.

I had not yet become acquainted with Sam or his casual homestead, way out in the country, so I asked him for directions. In our neck of the woods, the person giving directions usually starts by asking if you know where such-and-such Baptist church is.

Sometimes, if I say, "No," there's a silence on the other end of the line, as if the caller has hung up. But usually, the person is trying to think of the next nearest church—or the nearest crossroads country store—to get me started in the right direction. Once we get the church identified, then we get down to lefts and rights.

Tonight, Sam and I were lucky. We both knew the same church, so we got down to serious directions right away; I pulled on some clothes and was on my way.

The land lays nicely in this part of South Carolina. The hills rise and dip as they stretch in waves—until they loom up in the distance as a wall of mountains. Tonight, the closer hills were washed in gray and silver by the light of the full moon; those far away on the horizon were a black border, draped low against the soft blue-grayness of the sky.

Here and there, in yards of isolated farms, smeared circlets of pale blue light shone over sleeping houses. Not a lot of mischief upsets the peace of our countryside. But our folks see plenty on TV, and that mercury light is reassuring.

There weren't many cars on the road. The distance between mail boxes lengthened, and after a while, the yard lights were behind me. Sam was right when he said he lived "a right far piece out."

At last, I saw the steeple as I rounded a curve. The church sat high on a hill a short distance from the road. Its moonlit whiteness glowed, shadow-flecked amid a grove of black lace trees. Headstones in the graveyard looked like granite bookends.

Counting the turnoffs carefully, I turned into Sam's driveway at last, bouncing in the truck cab as the tires jarred against rocks in the deep ruts. Behind the house, someone signaled with a flashlight. I passed a jumble of swaybacked outbuildings, all built by Sam without a rule or a plumb line, just boards sort of attached together, each leaning in a different direction.

The man waved the beam in an arc over his head and walked in front of the truck, leading me along on the weedy track. He halted and the flashlight steadied, and he stepped up to the door of the truck and courteously opened it for me.

"Thanks for comin', Doc. Hate to call you out so late, but she still ain't had but the two little pigs all day, and the rest don't seem to be a-comin' like they ort to."

"No problem, Sam. Lead the way," I said, hauling my bag out of the truck and expecting him to clomp off to one of the tilted outbuildings. But Sam aimed his flashlight at the ground and walked along the hedges toward a deeper shadow a few feet away and stopped.

"She's in here."

"Where?" We had nearly bumped into a square, planked-up box. Well, not square—nothing on the place was square. But maybe trapezoid? It was about as high as our heads. The boards were warped and splintered, and the box had a decided tilt. The smell gave it away. I knew that odor all too well.

No door on this side. I walked to the corner and looked around. No door there, either. I peeped in through a crack, and there was the sow, just stretched out across the whole floor. And no way to get in. I looked back at Sam to get a clue.

"Just slide through there, Doc."

Sam aimed the beam at an opening, about two planks shy of the flat tin roof. Sam's pig delivery room was a doorless box.

I studied the sow's house and wondered how she got in. I decided it was built around her. She had just grown up in there. The smells—sour swill and ancient manure—told me that this was the pig's old homeplace.

This is going to be the worst pig story of all time, I thought. *Better get on with it.* I put the toes of my boots against the wall, pushed up and wedged my head and shoulders through the opening. A nail in the tin roof jabbed my head and tore a hole in my baseball cap. I yanked the cap tighter on my forehead, then pulled my stomach and hips up over those splintery boards.

Sam's light flashed through a crack in the planks, and I could see my patient below me, a white slab of Yorkshire sow flopped on her side. Under her hide, 400 pounds of fat shimmied as she sucked air. In the dim light, I could see her eyes. They were shiny as shellac. Two pink, wrinkled piglets, nuzzling the sow's teats, squirmed next to her big belly.

There are two kinds of mothers among sows: good and bad. Once in a while, a sow turns out to be a maternal rogue, and will kill her babies. But most are very, very protective mamas. If her piglet squeals, the good mama wants to know who's messing with her child and why. That kind of hog can turn mean in a heartbeat, ready to hang a tusk in the intruder. Despite their weight, pigs can move fast.

Sam's old sow appeared to be of the nurturing persuasion. Her glazed eyes sent me a warning that I took to heart. I thought, *Lord, you gotta help me! She's thinkin' she might just have me for breakfast!*

Hanging there—half in, half out of the box—I studied the boarded-up walls, knowing full well how much damage a pig can inflict on a human leg. I also pondered all the places I wanted these legs to take me in time to come. It didn't look promising. Somehow, I was going to have to improve my odds.

Sam stood behind me, fidgeting. Finally, I eased the rest of me inside the cramped box and stepped on the dirty slab floor. It crackled like a carton of eggs.

"What we need here is a door!" I muttered, clinching my teeth. The sow lifted her head, and her glinting eyes stared in my direction.

I knew if those piglets squealed, there was no way I could get out of here. I leaned through the opening and whispered: "Sam, you might need to ease in here and give me a hand."

"Sure thing, Doc."

I stepped sideways, against the wall, as Sam slung his skinny legs through the opening. My odds improved by 50 percent immediately: The sow now had four legs to attack, and the first set of legs would be Sam's. Perfect.

I sidestepped around to the back of the box. "Sam, can you stand there by her head and keep her happy?"

Sam stooped down, rubbed the sow's snout, and I let my breath out. My odds were now 100 percent better.

I got my own flashlight out of the bag to light up my patient's hindquarters, laid out my supplies and got down to business. I cleaned away the blood and dirt around the birth canal, then lubricated my hand and gently reached in. She didn't even flinch. She was all out of fight. My fingers found a soft bag wedged tightly. I could feel the bones of a spine where a small snout and head should be.

"She's got one hung up in the pelvic inlet," I told Sam. "It can't decide which way is out."

I turned the piglet, wrapped inside its protective birth sac, until it could slide into the pelvic inlet the normal way, then pulled it along the vaginal canal. I felt the sow's muscles give a faint contraction. She was back in business.

I quickly removed the rubbery placenta from the piglet and massaged its limp body with a towel. I was relieved to see it inhale and its lungs expand. Its heart pulsed softly against my hand as I dried the newborn. It was a boar.

I put it down beside the sow's belly near the two who were many hours older. I was pleased to see it scramble to its feet and head straight to the dinner table. Newborn pigs are so alert and agile, it's amazing.

With the logjam sorted out, the sow was able to pick up the natural rhythm of her birthing routine. The fourth little form was already coming down the canal and almost fell into my hands. I toweled it off. Sam and I grinned as we watched it shove its tiny shoulders in among the other three piglets now nursing gustily. The sow's double row of teats could accommodate at least 12, maybe 14, at one feeding. We had a few to go.

Except for the contented, tiny snuffles of the diners, we were quiet in the box. The night outside was still. Then, all of a sudden, a great long sigh: "Ooooh," and then a whisper, "There's another one!"

I looked around, startled.

Through the cracks in the wall, I could see bright eyes gleaming, reflecting the light of our flashlights. The pig box was surrounded by about a dozen little children. They must have sneaked out of their beds and slipped light-footed through the moonlight. I grinned as I glanced up and saw their eyes widen with excitement as they watched the miracle.

Every time a piglet emerged and took its first breath, a chorus of "Ooooh! There's another one!" hummed around the pig box—a soft musical chorus.

The children laughed at the way the baby pigs pushed and shoved each other aside in their search for the best milk supply, squealing in protest when another's sharp little hoof poked too deep in the free-for-all scramble. All at once, memories welled up. I remembered what it was like to be a kid, seeing an animal give birth for the first time, and being awed by the mystery of new life. Maybe delivering pigs wasn't so bad, after all.

Finally, the last of the litter emerged. The Yorkshire breathed easily now, her labor over. A long line of little pigs was plastered to the folds of mama's fat, and suckling sounds mingled with the sow's sighs and grunts.

I wiped my hands and arms, rolled up the soiled cloths, put them in a plastic bag and repacked my instruments. When I stood up, my knees cracked. I had been crouched in the pig box, oblivious to everything else, 'til my joints were groaning.

Sam and I heaved ourselves through the slit at the top of the box. Outside, the air smelled wonderfully sweet. I took a long deep breath, savoring it. Almost dazzled by the light of the moon, I could see Sam's face clearly. He was smiling. He slid down the wall to the ground, and was engulfed by a wad of children. They jumped around him, grabbing at his hands, his arms, his legs, all of them talking at once. He threw back his head and laughed as they chattered, so excited, then gently brushed them away. He pulled a ragged wallet out of his bib overalls, reached over the heads of his children and put some bills in my hand.

"I sure thank you, Doc," Sam said. He picked up the smallest child, settled it in the crook of an elbow, and wrapped his other arm around as many children as he could gather, tucking them close.

As I turned my truck around, the headlights flashed over the family. I could see them, outlined brightly against the dark hedges and the darker shadow of the doorless pig box.

I realized something there, that night, that I have since seen over and over: Joy and beauty turn up in what only *seem* to be the poorest places.

15

Sam and his kids cuddled together in the chilly night, their faces shining in the light of the moon, all smiling. I looked in the rearview mirror and saw a multitude of small hands, fluttering like lunar moths, waving good-bye.

Out on the highway, I settled back in the familiar comfort of the pickup truck seat and let out a satisfied sigh. My legs were sore, but mercifully still intact. Suddenly, I wondered if there were enough baby pigs to go around for all of Sam's children. I hoped so.

In the excitement, I had lost count. But it looked just about even.

Chapter 2

Jitterbugging With Helga

I hung my brand-new diploma from Tuskegee University's School of Veterinary Medicine on a wall at an emergency veterinary clinic in Greenville.

My first job as a certified D.V.M. was labor-intensive, to say the least.

The clinic's rotation system called for me to be on duty around the clock for one week, and have a little time off the next. I would work 94 hours at the clinic, grabbing a nap whenever I could. The following week, I would do relief work at other vets' clinics.

It was an exhausting introduction to veterinary medicine, but I thrived on it. It left no time to be nervous about being new and inexperienced. That assembly-line schedule, treating animals with all kinds of medical problems, was a sure-fire way to apply what I had learned from my professors. Only what I had learned wasn't always quite enough.

When that emergency clinic phone rang, any hour of the day or night, there was no telling what might be in trouble at the other end of the line. The truth is, sometimes it was better not to know.

One Sunday morning, I'd been on all week and was supposed to get off at noon. I was counting those last weary hours when the phone rang. A heavily-accented European voice nearly spilled tears through the receiver: "Help me! Help me! Won't nobody help me?"

"What's your problem, sir?" I asked.

His speech was a far cry from the upland Southern drawl familiar to my ears. "My Helga," the man cried, "she very sick and nobody help her. I call everywhere and nobody help my Helga!"

"Who is Helga?" I asked.

"My anaconda. Helga is my 15-foot anaconda."

Whew. "I see why nobody will help you," I wanted to say. "You're telling me too quick." But he was so desperate, I said, "Uh, what seems to be wrong with Helga?"

"She ate two rabbits two days ago, but now she very sick." He made me understand that Helga was suffering from irregularity of the bowels. She was constipated.

Treating constipated snakes had not been high on my priority list, and I doubted that there was a great catalog of work written about the problem. With the phone cradled on my shoulder, I got down a book with a section on reptiles and started flipping through "Snakes." Sure enough, I found this little bit about constipation; there was a medicine to inject. It said in parentheses to make *sure* to stick the needle underneath the scales, not through. Don't ask why.

"Bring her on in," I said. "I can't leave the clinic."

"I can't!" he wailed. "You have to come here! Hurry! Hurry!" It was just too pitiful.

I checked the supply cabinet, and lo and behold, we had the remedy. I got directions from the guy. When I got off at noon, I filled a syringe and tooled over to the fairgrounds, outside Greenville, armed with the injection and very limited knowledge.

Helga's keeper was a Yugoslavian snake handler, traveling in America with a carnival. When he discovered that morning that the star of his show was sick, he began calling veterinary offices listed in the yellow pages. Most of the offices were closed for the weekend, and the few he reached said they couldn't help.

As I was driving out there, I thought about their reasons. Fifteen feet of anaconda. Hmm. That's as tall as me, one of my brothers and half of another one—provided you could convince the three of us to lie down head-to-toe beside his snake. I had the creeps, and I didn't know anything—yet.

The snake handler's 18-wheeler was parked near the midway. The smell of last night's hot dogs, hamburgers, cotton candy and oily popcorn mingled with the aroma of the animals in the cattle shed and trampled sawdust.

Faded lettering and pictures on the side of the reptile show's trailer touted the wonders and marvels inside: deadly serpents collected from all over the world, just waiting to thrill anyone willing to part with a dollar. If I'd come to the fair on my own hook, I'd have spent my dollar another way. But now I had no option. I stepped right up—into a truckload of snakes.

I walked into a maze—went in weaving through boxes. They were stacked to the ceiling. Full of snakes. Boxes and cages, arranged so that they formed a pathway leading deep into the cave-like quarters. Near the cab, I could see a canvas bed suspended from the ceiling. *The snake handler lives in here*, I thought. *He sleeps in here. With Helga, his 15-foot anaconda, and all her kind.*

Making myself thin as possible, I walked down the middle of the path between the boxes. A sudden beans-in-a-hollow-gourd sound rattled at my elbow. I jumped back, just as the snake handler hurried up, grabbed my hand and welcomed me to his home.

It was actually pretty clean in there. It didn't smell bad or anything; snakes don't "go" that often, and they don't create much of an odor, or a lot of mess.

Under the snake handler's bed, there was a huge box lined with air holes along the sides. That was where Helga lived. I guess they would lie there at night and tell each other bedtime stories.

The snake handler unlatched the box's lid and raised it slowly. Rays from the overhead light pierced the darkness inside the box. At first, all I could see were coils, intertwined and wrapped around themselves. Coils big as my leg. A pot of super-sized spaghetti cooked too long and left out overnight. That box was just plain full of snake.

This was Helga. Constipated Helga.

It was interesting how quickly Helga had become an entity, almost a person, to me. It may have been the way the Yugoslavian lovingly called her by name, or maybe it was because I believed something that big was entitled to respect. I could understand her owner's wish to have Helga purged and happy again. Fifteen feet is a lot of misery.

Then she raised her head. That head, about as big as my two hands, rose up and moved smoothly from side to side as her eyes searched the open space above her.

She spotted me, but I was still a stranger to her at that point in our relationship. We had not progressed to the bonding which, ideally, unites a doctor and his patient. She was a lot calmer than I was. Every sweat gland in my body turned loose at once.

My mind was on her teeth. She was not poisonous; she didn't need to be. An anaconda has jaws, lower and upper, chock-full of crescent-shaped teeth. Once those strong teeth lock into the prey, they can hold on forever, if they want to. The only way to get those teeth out is to slip something flat, like a thin piece of metal, behind them and push them out. Once the teeth latch onto something, then those coils begin to hug. Anacondas' hugs are world-famous.

Remembering this, I walked slowly along her bed toward the other end of Helga, eyeing the pile of coils, looking for a tell-tale bulge as I went. Somewhere in that mess of spaghetti was the residue of a pair of rabbits—if the snake handler's diagnosis was correct—and the cause of Helga's discomfort. My game plan was to lift a coil, slip the needle under a scale, plunge the liquid into Helga and get the heck outta there.

"If you'll just hold her head, sir. Can you do that?" I was glad my voice still worked. The snake handler nodded, smiling. No problem. He ranked as one brave man in my book.

I saw a coil rising. *Between the scales,* I reminded myself. *Between the scales!*

I slipped my left hand under Helga's upthrust thick tube, preparing to push the plunger of the syringe in my right hand. Ready, aim, fire!

Helga had another plan. Her coil continued to ascend like a motorized upside-down U. I rammed the loop under my armpit, using the elbow-lock hold that works for most animals. I'm pretty strong, but to Helga, I was just a feather-weight nuisance.

My feet rose off the floor. I was airborne. The coil kept rising upward, and I scrambled to get a toehold on the floor. That coil rose until I was bumping the ceiling, but still hanging on.

Coil after coil of Helga spilled out of the box. She sashayed this way and that, flinging me from one side of the trailer to the other. She was jitterbugging—and I never did like to dance.

Helga's handler did his own little dance as he dodged her writhing, lashing body. I would have been thrilled if he had cut in. My feet and free arm jerked about as Helga flung herself (and me) in loops

22

and spirals, trying to free herself. I dared not let go. Back and forth, from one wall to the other, we twirled. My head banged on a corner of a metal box. Stars twinkled before my eyes. More bad thoughts: *What if that box comes down and a pit viper falls on top of me?*

Do something, Orr! my brain was screaming.

I realized I was still gripping the needle in my free hand. Forget what the book said. No way could I slip this needle under a scale. In desperation, I slammed the syringe into the jitterbugging coils, emptied my arms of Helga and jumped out the door.

How was the guy going to get her back in the box? I don't know. They were on a personal basis. It was none of my business. As I beat it from the truck, I yelled over my shoulder. "Call me tomorrow...."

He did. It was bad news. The injection had failed. Her bowels were still blocked. Helga was even more unhappy. Apparently something else was wrong. She had to be X-rayed. So I took off for the fairgrounds in my little old Ford truck; we pushed and shoved Helga's box into the back and brought her to the clinic.

The clinic was my turf, and I intended to let her know who was in charge. Besides, we had her outnumbered this time. Counting me, her handler and the clinic's veterinary technician, the ratio of man to snake was much better. And I was primed and ready for Helga.

The second she raised her huge head, I had a roll of cotton gauze ready. My arm whirled like a fan-blade set on high speed as I wrapped her mouth. Her owner wailed, "Watch out for the eyes! Watch out for the eyes!" I was watching out for the teeth.

She looked like a relic from an Egyptian pyramid. We hoisted her onto the X-ray table, stretched Helga under the lens and took the picture. Then slid her up the table, X-rayed another few feet. We did this until we ran out of Helga.

Back into the box she went. We removed the gauze and slammed the lid down almost before she was aware she had been de-mummified.

Examining the film, I was disappointed. No sign of a blockage. No sign of the rabbits; they were thoroughly digested. She was not constipated. Back to the books.

I put a fecal smear under the scope and saw the soiurce of her problem. She was suffering from an intestinal infection, one that should respond to oral medication.

A snake's anatomy adds new meaning to administering oral medication, or in plain terms, giving a patient a pill. You have to insert a lubricated tube far enough down the throat for the pill or capsule to slide into the stomach. Recalling Helga's previous reaction to my tender care, I decided her handler was on better personal terms with her than I. After all, they practically slept together. I told him how to administer the pills, then provided him with a tube and an ample supply of tetracycline.

Earlier, as he watched me study the X-rays, the Yugoslavian was so thrilled to see his snake's innards that you'd have thought we were looking at pictures of his family.

"Would you like to have these?" I had asked him.

He nodded excitedly. "Yes. Yes. My wife, I'll send them to my wife! She will be so happy to see Helga!"

I put the X-rays back in the cabinet to dry a few more minutes while I did the other tests on Helga. When the Yugoslavian was ready to leave, I grabbed the X-rays out of the dark cabinet, slipped them in a large manila envelope and handed the package to him.

Back we went to the fairgrounds, where the carnival crews were packing up to leave the following morning for the next town on their tour. I told the Yugoslavian to call if Helga had not improved within a few days, and said my goodbyes. He was so grateful that I was almost embarrassed.

Later that evening, as I put things back in place at the clinic, I saw some X-rays in the dryer. I held one to the light. Ribs, vertebrae. Ribs, vertebrae. On and on. It was Helga. More film, more Helga. All Helga. Missing were the X-rays of a dog.

The snake handler never called back, so I guess Helga recovered. But every now and then this funny picture pops into my mind: I see a housewife somewhere in Yugoslavia opening a flat manila envelope sent to her from her husband in the United States. I still wonder what she must have thought, and said, when she discovered he had sent her X-rays of a dog.

Chapter 3

Black Butter

The keepers of the family farms in this hill country are an independent lot. Probably that's so everywhere; it takes a particular mind set to put so much faith in Heaven and nature and so little in "public work"— that's what our folks call being on a factory payroll.

Life experience, and sometimes education, have taught these farmers a lot about taking care of their land and livestock. When one asks for help, he's definitely got a problem.

So when my old friend Chad called for a hand with his gimpy cow, I knew he had trouble. And I was probably going to have some, too. Chad's cows are notorious free-thinkers.

When the call came in, I was sewing up the torn leg of a dog our banker loves. While that dog was lying on the table, getting his scars patched over, he was already curling his lip in a sweet dream about his next fight. I knew he'd be back soon when I said goodbye to him and his long-suffering owner. Then, quickly, I told our receptionist I would be gone for a while. Half an hour later, I drove through the gate at Chad's old homeplace.

Chad's rambling two-story house sits on a hill with an awesome view, the crowning point of a 700-acre farm which has been in his family at least four generations. The house appears to have changed little as it passed down from father to son, though Chad has covered the old clapboards with vinyl siding.

It is a place of quiet comfort. The wrap-around porch is lined with old rockers, where you can rest and look out over green, ever-rolling beauty. Cottonwoods and river birches line the banks of a shallow creek in the bottoms. In summer, the stream is shady, cool, inviting.

From the bottoms, the land ascends in terraces and hills; those closest to the house are covered with lush grass. Some of the hills have been cleared to make rough pasture land; others are dark with thick stands of pine or hardwood. Faint tracks lace the hilly land together—paths carved year after year by herds of cattle, wagons, trucks and tractors taking the course of least resistance across the rolling landscape.

Finally, and best of all, a curtain of purple and blue hangs in the distance—the serrated tops of the Blue Ridge Mountains, dividing the Carolinas. I never tire of the sight of this range that wraps its arms around the land I love best in all the world.

I knew from past experience that before I could treat Chad's cow, we had to find her. My trips out to his farm often turn into search-and-rescue missions that take more time than I ought to spend, but I love coming out here. It's good for the soul.

I stopped at the back door and honked the horn. Chad came out, slid into the passenger seat and pointed in the general direction of where he had last seen his crippled cow.

A hard-packed track leads out of the barnyard, follows a narrow ridge, then swoops down and crosses the top of a dam that makes a deep pond. The narrow track atop the earthen dam is the lone road connecting the barnyard with the hills where his cattle graze.

The dark bodies of Chad's mixed-breed cattle looked like paper cutouts against the grassy meadows. We drove over the dam and started searching for the lame cow. Chad's cattle are Black Baldies, developed by crossing Herefords with Angus cattle. Half-wild, they only come in contact with humans when Chad or some of his helpers throw out hay bales in winter, or when they are rounded up for market. They spook easily.

At last, we spotted a tell-tale silhouette against the horizon: a three-legged cow, alone. Sometimes a sick cow or bull considers anything that comes near it as a predator and gets very defensive. Often, it leaves the herd and goes off on its lonesome. What's more, a sick animal is unpredictable.

I circled wide behind this Black Baldy, creeping along until I could get close enough to scope out the situation.

"Her stomach is tucked up," I said. "She's been off her feed a few days. That front hoof is badly swollen. She's either got a bad case of foot rot, or else she's got a stob or something jammed between her toes."

I was betting on a stob. The pastures had been bush-hogged recently, leaving behind patches of saber-sharp stumps of sumac and other bushes. A stob can pierce the tender flesh between the toes of a cow's cloven hoof—the only part of the hard pad that is susceptible to punctures—and it's not unusual for such wounds to get infected.

We were a couple of truck lengths from the crippled cow when she twisted awkwardly to face us. To her, the truck was a bigger danger than the buzzards and wild dogs she most feared, and her defenses were up. Her ears were erect, twitching nervously; every sound was a threat. She had a demented look in her eyes. I'd seen that look too many times to ignore it.

"Chad, this cow is on the fight. She's crazy with pain," I said. "She's wild enough to be dangerous. There's no way we can work on her out here. We'll have to drive her with the truck, get her back to the corral."

She pinned us with her eyeballs and lowered her head as I let off the brake, and we rolled closer. The trick here was to intimidate her just enough to get her moving toward the barnyard, without enraging her. If she attacked the truck, she could do a lot of damage to herself—not to mention my truck.

She whirled away from the truck on three legs and retreated, shivering when the swollen hoof touched the ground. Talk about slow. If it wasn't so exasperating, it would have been funny. If we got too close, she halted, turned and stared at us, daring us not to stop. Then, taking her own sweet time, she got moving again and we crept along. At long last, we zig-zagged our way to the road across the dam.

"Now we've got her aimed in the right direction, Jerry," Chad said optimistically. "We got it made."

The words were hardly out of his mouth when she turned sideways smack in the middle of the dam and aimed her glittering eyes at us. She'd had enough. She was taking her stand.

I'd had just about enough, too. We were blocked. The road across the dam was a narrow single track, with no room to maneuver. If she charged the truck, we'd be in trouble: deep water on one side, a deep ravine on the other. We couldn't go forward. We couldn't go back.

Cussing the cow, we eased out of the truck, closing the doors softly. I didn't want to startle her. I motioned for Chad to move toward the ditch below the dam, next to a barbed-wire fence that kept his cattle out of a swampy area. *That seems a pretty safe place for him,* I thought. I got my lariat out of the truck bed and eased toward the cow.

All of a sudden, Chad threw up his arms and hollered. Maybe he thought the unexpected noise might prod her toward the barn. If so, his plan backfired. If you think I was surprised, you should have seen the cow. She forgot her aching foot in a heartbeat. A black flash whizzed off the dam and tore off after Chad. He reacted instinctively. With a great leap, he went over the barbed-wire. Almost. One boot snagged on the top wire. He landed on all fours in the swamp, entangled in cattails, clumps of grass and mud.

Chad's hoisted fanny was a perfect target. The cow didn't even pause at the fence. Taking the strands with her, she slammed her head against his rear end. He tried to get up, and *bam!* She hit him again.

"She's gonna kill you!" I yelled at Chad. As if he didn't know! I knew I had to do something, so I wound the lariat into loops and raced down the bank. I slapped her rump sharply with the rope to get her attention. I succeeded. She paused in her assault on Chad's fanny, turned her head and spotted another enemy. Me.

I swatted her head with the lariat, hoping it would befuddle her long enough for Chad to get away. But the lariat trick backfired. A loop that any rodeo star would have envied circled like a necklace around her throat. The rope enraged her even more. She spun in my direction and charged. I started running, my head thrown back, my arms pumping, hauling a crazy cow in my wake as I sprinted toward a nearby oak.

Her hooves thundered in my ears. I was in deep trouble: I couldn't drop the lariat and have that cow dragging it behind her. She could fall and break her leg or her neck. I sure as heck wanted to get that rope off her neck. But even more, I wanted to keep my tailbone out of harm's way. I reached the oak and flung myself upward. My fingers latched onto a limb. Hauling the rest of myself across the branch, I leaned against the trunk, gasping for air.

The enraged cow stopped just inches shy of the trunk. Her chest heaved, and her nostrils pumped like bellows as she sucked air. I stared down at my patient.

Dang it, I thought, *this really looks professional!*

Back at the dam, Chad was hobbling toward the truck, rubbing muddy hands against his rear end. He slid under the steering wheel and backed off the dam. Spraying dirt and grass under the tires, he aimed the truck at the oak. I sat on my lofty perch and considered my options: If I could get my end of the lariat wrapped around the branch enough times to take up the slack, she'd be trapped.

I dangled my foot in her face, baiting the trap. The cow swirled in anger, charging closer; the rope drooped. Quickly, I wrapped another loop around the branch. Finally, she was almost hanging from the limb.

31

I slid down the other side of the tree, ran to the truck for my bag, and filled a syringe with trusty old Rompum, a vet's best friend. The anesthesia went straight to her pain-addled brain.

A short while later, her eyelids fluttered. I loosened the lariat as she said her bovine prayers and laid herself down to sleep. Examining her swollen foot, I saw that a stob had done its worst. I gave the hoof a good cleansing, lanced the pus-filled swelling and probed deeper into the wound with forceps. An embedded sliver of wood finally emerged. Cleaning the inflamed tissue again, I gave her an injection of a long-acting antibiotic.

Chad and I sat in the truck a short distance away and watched the cow sleep off the anesthesia. After 15 minutes, she roused and scrambled to her feet awkwardly. Out of habit, she tried to protect her injured hoof. She was still a bit groggy, but the demented look was gone. Limping slightly, she trudged off toward a bunch of cows and began grazing. I started the truck. Broom sedge crackled under the tires.

"Lookahere, Chad," I said, "you really ought to get some lime out here, get rid of all this brush and sumac. I'm gonna charge you double if these stobs punch through my tires."

He just grinned, shifted his sore tail against the leather seat and poked a chew of Red Man in his cheek as we bumped along toward the house.

Chapter 4

Last of the Georgia Belles

Some folks hate to answer the telephone. They think it's a nuisance or an invasion of privacy, but the ringing of the phone is the pulse of a vet's profession. Like a kid, I feel a twinge of suspense as I wonder what kind of crisis has prompted this call.

Most of the time, it's just routine—at least for me or my associates, Jim and Ron; but for the caller, it can be a time of deep anxiety. And once in a while, an adventure rings our bell. These calls make life exciting.

Late one evening, I got such a call while I was sculpting a wing of a wild turkey. It was for a clay model that I would later cast in bronze. Sculpting is my hobby. Since animals are what I know best, I find a lot of challenge and pleasure in creating their likenesses.

I put the sculpture aside to pick up the phone. Immediately, a familiar voice boomed in my ear.

"Jerry!" Willie hollered, "I know a feller who has two black bear cubs he's trying to get rid of. You want 'em?"

Willie's a friend of long standing—a hunter whose rambles and hunts have led him all over the South to visit friends who love to hunt as much as he does. Where and when Willie goes depends upon the type of game in season. And when somebody in his far-flung network needs help, he's the man they call. More times than I can count, he has passed the buck to me. Sometimes literally.

"Willie," I answered, "I really don't have any use for a pair of cubs right now, but if he's got a problem, I'll try to find them a home."

The solution that instantly popped in my mind was the farm of my friend Toby, to whom I have been known to pass a buck or so. Toby lives way back up in the remotest part of the county. The nearest crossroads store is about four miles from Toby's farm, which nestles in a heavily-wooded fold in the mountains. His place offered plenty of space for cubs to roam, and I knew he would take good care of them.

Toby is one of the toughest, yet kindest-hearted men I know, especially when it comes to animals. My partners and I have seen him take care of a sick or hurt animal as tenderly as a mother hovering over a hurting child. So I had no qualms about asking him to adopt two little homeless black bears.

What's more, I knew Toby's reputation in the community would be added protection for the bears. Toby is a man who takes nothing off anyone. He minds his business and expects everybody else to do the same. Only a blamed fool would dare mess with anything that belonged to Toby.

I told Willie I'd check out an idea and get back in touch. Then I dialed Toby's number. Willie likes quick answers, and I knew he would worry me to death if I didn't get something done quickly.

As I waited for Toby to come to the phone, I thought about something that happened a couple of years earlier, an incident that taught me a lot about the kind of man he is.

It is Toby's pleasure to ride horseback in the mountains surrounding his property. That way, he can keep a close eye on the animal trails in the forest, and get an idea where game is plentiful when it is time to re-stock his freezer and the smokehouse.

On that particular day, he and his horse were deep in the mountains, where neighbors were few and far between. They came to a fallen-down, sorry-looking house that had become the hangout of a motorcycle gang. A bunch of bikers lolled around their machines in the yard. A couple of riders sat in the saddles of dusty cycles, joyfully varrooming the motors, going nowhere. The ground was littered with crushed beer cans, broken glass bottles, rusting engine parts and bald tires.

Toby nodded to the group under the trees and lifted a hand to his hat brim, not speaking. Men in our country do that to acknowledge the presence of a stranger without appearing over-friendly or invading the person's privacy.

Some of the men in the yard returned the greeting, equally silent. The only sounds were the throaty throbs of the motorcycles and the plop-plop of the hooves of Toby's horse on the dirt road.

That peaceful passage was suddenly interrupted when a growling pit bull rushed in fury from under the porch. It loped through the trashy yard, its paws churning dust and gravel as it dashed under Toby's sorrel. The dog lunged and clamped its steely jaws onto the flesh just under the horse's left front leg. The pit bull's teeth sank deep into the pectoral muscles.

Toby's horse reared and circled on its back hooves, pawing at the sky. It wheeled and bucked, trying to shake the dog off, but the demon hung on as if its mouth were stapled to the horse's chest.

The sorrel fell, shivering with pain, in the road. As the horse crumpled, Toby swung his boots from the stirrups and jumped clear just as the animals hit the dirt together.

Toby, whose marksmanship medals were rusting in an old Army trunk in his attic, always wore a pistol in a holster on his hip when he was out riding. He pulled the .22 out, steadied the barrel with his left hand, aimed carefully at the dog, still clamped on his horse's belly, and squeezed the trigger.

Before the sharp crack of the exploding bullet rolled across the yard, that pit bull was dead. Its jaws sagged loose from the sorrel.

The horse struggled to its feet and stood trembling in the road; blood flowed down its leg and dropped in red splotches on the dirt.

Toby shoved his .22 back in its holster. He stalked into the yard, plowing through the middle of the bikers, who watched in silence as he stomped up the rickety steps. A motorcycle engine died with a quiet cough as Toby's fist banged on the door. He was about to hit the door again when it was flung open by a frowning, wide-eyed man hastily stuffing a T-shirt into dirty jeans.

"I just shot your dog," Toby snarled.

The men in the yard neither moved nor made a sound. The man at the door stared at Toby. He looked out over Toby's shoulder and saw his dead dog; he looked at the horse, then back at Toby. The man stood there for a minute, then muttered, "Yessir."

Toby told me what happened later in the day when he brought his injured horse to our clinic. He talked, still angry, as I sewed up the mangled flesh and muscles on his horse's chest, then gave it antibiotic and tetanus shots.

Toby hated to kill the dog, he said, but he had no choice. He was mad because that pit bull had been trained to be mean and to attack. He thought the breed had gotten a bad rap.

Yes, Toby seemed the natural man to take care of some abandoned cubs, I figured, and when he finally answered the phone, he agreed that was so. The only thing was, I told him, the cubs were living in captivity in a swamp down in Florida.

"No problem," he told me. "I need a little vacation anyway."

Over the next few days, Toby fixed the cubs a safe place in a remote corner of his woods. Then he converted the bed of his Toyota pickup into a sturdy cage and headed south with his Uncle Bud.

A couple of weeks later, Toby gave this account of his Florida vacation:

He found the bears, all right, following Willie's directions. But what he found were "cubs" that had done a lot of growing—a big boar and a sow, immensely fat from being raised in a pen in a South Florida swamp. The boar alone weighed 600 pounds. The minute he saw them, Toby knew it would take two trips to cart both bears to the South Carolina mountains.

The size of the bears was not the only surprise in store for Toby and his uncle. He had expected Willie's friend to be on hand to help load the bears. When they drove up in the yard of the rag-tag swamp shack, a woman who looked older than sin came out on the porch.

Toby asked where her husband was. The old ha'nt gave him a meaningful dark look. "They in the swamp," she said. The menfolks of this family were in the swamp going about their business, and whatever their business was, it was none of Toby's business.

Crowded around her at the doorway were four or five barefooted teen-age girls.

"Every single one of those girls was pregnant, and acted mighty proud about it," Toby said.

Toby asked the old woman where the bears were, and she pointed to the back of the house. He drove around the shack and backed the Toyota up to the pen, where the bears waddled their fat haunches, pacing back and forth inside a rickety fence.

The pregnant girls waddled to the back of the shack. They squatted on the steps, snickering as they watched Toby and his uncle sweat and strain to get the boar into the cage on the truck.

The girls giggled and prattled, cutting their eyes at the two men to make sure their visitors noticed them. It would have been hard not to. Their voices carried loud and clear in the pine thicket; their vocabulary was so foul, the buzzards in the dead snags turned their heads in shame.

Toby had been around some mighty rough-talking soldiers when he was in the army. He knew a few colorful terms himself. But that bunch of raunchy gals got his goat. He was appalled; poor God-fearing, church-going Uncle Bud was embarrassed nearly to death.

Toby said he could see his uncle cringe as the girls flaunted their swollen, half-clothed selves. They laughed at Uncle Bud's mortified face and tried to out-vamp one another to make him blush.

Finally, Toby's uncle could not stand the dirty talk one minute more. Uncle Bud opened the truck door and grabbed a bag of sun-ripened Georgia Belles he had bought at a roadside peach stand as they drove down. Uncle Bud shoved the bag of peaches toward the girls.

"If you'll just stop cussing and swearing, I'll give you these peaches," he promised.

The harpies cackled happily and snatched the bag. After a squabble among themselves over the spoils, they settled down on the steps to eat the Georgia Belles. Their teeth chomped through the fuzzy skin and pink juice dripped down their chins and onto their fat bellies.

For a while, it was nice and quiet in the swamp. Finally, the caged bear was loaded in the bed of the pickup. The Toyota's springs creaked as the rear end sank down almost to the axle.

One final slurp came from the steps as the last of the peaches disappeared.

Then, just as Toby and Uncle Bud got in the truck, one of the lovelies waddled up to Toby's uncle and poked the empty bag through the open window.

"Hey, Mister!" she ordered, "when you all come back, brang us some more of them %*@&*! peaches."

Chapter 5

Blindsided

One morning, I walked out of our farm house, leaving Betsy and our sleepy-eyed Ethan eating breakfast. Before long, that four-year-old would be wide awake, and his mama would have her hands full. But at that rare moment, it was quiet on our hilltop.

Along with my coffee, I drank in the air of a wonderfully peaceful morning. Early morning haze rose in wisps from the valley streams and lightly veiled the mountains that arc around us to the north. Men and machinery at the old rock quarry nearby had not yet cranked up for their day's work.

The Liberty Quarry has a dual life. A quarry may not sound like an ideal neighbor for lovers of the green and wild, but this old chiseled-down mound of granite is also a wildlife preserve. Foxes, beavers, all kinds of birds, other wildlife, and even an occasional bear, live in remarkable harmony with the giant machines that gouge and grind quartz-bearing rock. The crushed stone is hauled away to road and construction projects all over the western Carolinas and Georgia.

I looked toward the quarry lake, hoping to see a red-tailed hawk catching the early morning updrafts. I see one frequently. It may or may not be Rastus. But I am always looking.

Rastus was a wounded fledgling that came to the clinic about a year ago. He was brought in by a forest ranger when he was just a little fluff of feathers. We raised him out here on the farm. There is a lot of joy in watching a bird like that grow into a graceful, self-sufficient adult hawk.

It takes time and a lot of patience to raise such a bird, and to get it ready to go back to the wild. There are also tugging moments when this creature, that has become a demanding, squawking part of our lives, discovers independence, and takes off on its own.

We watched as Rastus made his first tentative ventures into the air above the farm. The flights became longer as he began to find food in the fields and woodlands nearby.

For a while, like many a human fledgling, he still showed up for breakfast. He was intimidating. Soaring and circling, he would lock his gaze on the chunks of raw meat we put on the deck railing. Then he made his landing approach, swift as a missile. My impulse was to duck, as those great wings and talons swooped down. But he would flip on his landing gear and hit the target perfectly, clutch up the meat and depart.

It was a wistful passage on the morning my whistle went unheeded. I knew Rastus was at last in his natural element. I felt a sense of satisfaction. I also felt loss. His time with us was a gift we will always treasure.

I know that for years to come, we won't quit looking. As I was looking, on that perfect morning, I realized I had been gathering wool a long time. Now I had work to do on the farm. The cool air of the morning would be gone too soon and, before too long, summer heat would drench our world in sweat.

The hawk was just one of the memories that clung like cobwebs as I loaded cattle and hauled them to another pasture. As I worked, images of the people and events, good and ill, that had shaped my life drifted through my mind. I mulled over the experiences that led to a career that I loved, to this hilltop home I shared with a wife and child who made me feel complete. I had never dared dream of this kind of fulfillment when I packed my duffel bag, after wasting my youth unwillingly in Southeast Asia.

I came home from Vietnam with serious questions about the meaning and value of the past four years of my life. Culture shock slapped me in the face when I got back to the States. Restless and uncertain about what I wanted to do with the rest of my life, I was typical of most veterans who survived that war.

About the only good that I could see coming out of my service in Uncle Sam's Navy were a couple of resolutions I made, based on lessons I learned in 'Nam. I intended to make these resolutions the touchstone of future decisions.

The first: I would never again complain about what I ate. The second: I would do something for the community, something that would make a difference, not just for myself, but also for my friends and others who did not come home from Vietnam. I felt I owed them a debt. I felt guilty because I had lived and so many others had died, or suffered atrocious injuries.

To tell the truth, I was not the military's most shining example. I joined the Navy straight out of high school. By the time I got to Southeast Asia, I wanted answers to questions that my superiors didn't think I should ask. After I told my superior officers that they were playing a silly game with their little war, I was promoted to K.P.

That assignment didn't begin too badly. I started out as a doorman at the mess hall. My duty was to make sure each man who came through the chow line had a pass. According to the regulations, anyone who didn't have a pass couldn't eat. That made no sense to me. It was just further proof of what I considered military-bureaucratic crap. To turn anyone away because he didn't have a slip of paper went against everything my mama taught me.

A platoon of Marines pitted my Southern hospitality against the military's rigidity. The leathernecks marched by the mess hall at mealtime, returning from two weeks in the bush. They had been without baths, hot food or rest the entire time. Grungy and starving, they caught a whiff of the day's main course: steak. The platoon leader trudged over to the mess hall where I was guarding the door.

"Is there any way I can get my men in there to eat?" he asked.

One look at those tired, dirty faces was enough.

"Sure," I said. "Welcome."

Uncle Sam's watchdog chewed my tail. I got another promotion: coffee maker. I dumped the entire contents of a five-pound bag of coffee in the first batch I made. You had to twist off a sip.

I didn't keep that job long. I was promoted to slinging hash. Plopping mashed potatoes from pot to plate with a huge spoon soon lost its glamour. The soldier who saved me from terminal boredom came through the line talking excitedly to a friend.

Gesturing wildly as he talked, he scooted his tray along the line with one hand, flailing the air with the other. I watched his approach with anticipation. My timing had to be just right. Ready...(load the ladle with a big helping of squishy spuds)...Aim...(hold the ladle steady)...Fire!

Bull's eye! His hand turned upward and a mound of warm potatoes slopped over his palm.

He wanted a fist fight, but I wasn't in the mood. I tonked him soundly on the top of his head with the ladle to settle his nerves. Uproar on the line.

Would you believe it? Another promotion. Dish washer detail. I got to stack hot dripping plates, cups and utensils to dry after they had been scoured and rinsed. Reading a Louis L'Amour book was more fun. Before long, the plates and utensils were piling up on the floor, in violation of the rule book.

That's how I landed the job of hauling garbage. Through rapid promotions, I had finally reached the end of the military ladder. I was as low as you could possibly climb.

I knew about garbage hauling. As a high school student, I lived for a while at the Greene's hog farm in northern Greenville County. One of my chores was to haul 55-gallon drums of discarded food from the dining hall at Furman University to the farm. We would dump the leftovers into a big boiler, and cook the scraps to feed the hogs. Hot swill flowed through a chute from the boiler into the troughs. When the tin chute clattered against the sides of the trough, the hogs came running from every direction.

In Vietnam, starving villagers came running. The base's garbage went into a landfill in the marsh. We dumped everything there—rusted vehicles, packing crates, burned planes, table scraps, plastic jugs, you name it. The throw-away philosophy followed an American tradition that was widely practiced until recycling became fashionable.

When I manhandled the 55-gallon drums off the trash truck, I could see the Vietnamese moving over the mounds of stinking garbage. They instantly headed for the spot where I was pouring a load of "fresh" trash. I had to be careful, because I couldn't bear to dump it on any of those desperate people.

They grabbed bits of bread, meat, vegetables and stuffed our leftovers in their battered containers. Often a tug-of-war would break out when plastic milk bags hit the pile. The villagers fought to get the ounce or two of milk already souring in the heat.

It was terrible to see proud people reduced to such a desperate state. I thought about the troughs at the farm back home, where we cooked food scraps to make it safe for the pigs to eat. At the landfill in Da Nang, watching old men, women and children scavenging for our rotting leftovers, I decided I would be forever grateful for whatever I had to eat.

Those people couldn't till their own soil. Bombs, bullets, mines and invaders had destroyed their crops, their cattle, their fields, their homes, their hopes. The Vietnamese didn't even know if they would wake up the next morning. For that matter, neither did we.

War does dreadful things to people.

In Vietnam, I saw people die—not only strangers, but also people I knew, cared for, depended on—and their deaths were a terrible waste. Vietnam was a war in which everybody lost something important. I decided that, if and when I got back home, I would never be a loser again.

Because of my "Vietnam resolutions," I had decided to become a veterinarian. It was the best way I could think of to put something back into the community. I worked to pay my way through Clemson University, saving my GI Bill for graduate school. I spent the summer between my Clemson freshman and sophomore years repairing fences for a car dealer who had a cattle farm not too far from the university.

I had been digging post holes and stringing wire at Mr. Warders' farm for a few days when I noticed a young white-faced steer behaving strangely. He followed the same pattern day after day—staying next to the fence, looking neither left nor right. The calf usually kept his nose close to the ground—but at the slightest noise, he jerked his head up. His ears twisted like radar scanners.

Moving slowly, the young bull nibbled grass growing along the fence, until he eventually arrived at the creek in a deep ravine. He had worn a path down the red clay bank. He spent a lot of time in the creek bed, drinking and cooling off in the shade of the overhanging trees. When he moved out of the creek, he followed a well-marked path leading to a thicket of trees and briars on a hill further away.

The bull weighed 500 pounds, but he was thinner than most of the herd—because the rest of them could graze without fear, far and wide on the lush grass of meadows near the creek and on the open ridge.

One morning as he ambled by, I stood quietly and looked at his eyes. They were clouded with a whitish film; the eyelids were red and weepy-looking. The calf had pink eye.

Though I was not qualified to diagnose a lot of bovine diseases, I had been raised on a dairy farm, and I knew what pink eye was. If it wasn't treated, Mr. Warders' calf could suffer a ruptured cornea. Pink eye was also an infectious disease that could spread to other cattle in the herd.

I remembered when my dad or neighboring farmers fitted big, black, cup-shaped blinders on the heads of cows with pink eye. The blinders protected their eyes from light and dust, but they looked like Mickey Mouse hats and made us kids laugh. Now I knew that pink eye caused blindness and was no laughing matter.

I telephoned Mr. Warders and told him about the calf. The next morning, the cattle farmer showed up at the pasture in a shiny, new, four-wheel-drive Jeep pickup from his car lot.

"Get in," he said. "I've brought a dose of penicillin for that calf. We'll have to find it and lasso it so I can give it a shot."

I was only in pre-vet courses, but I seriously doubted that one shot would be enough for an advanced case of pink eye.

Off we roared. I showed him the calf's path in the pasture, and we followed it until we saw the yearling lying under some oaks near the fence.

"This is a piece of good luck," he said. "It ought to be pretty simple now. Let's get this over with. I got a very busy day ahead."

An hour later, we were still bouncing over the terraces in the pasture and fording the creek in our attempt to corral the calf. The little bull was super-sensitive to sound because of his blindness. We weren't able to get anywhere close.

I suggested Mr. Warders let me out at the ravine with a rope; when the calf came down the bank, I would snag him and tie up his legs so Mr. Warders could administer the shot.

"That's a good idea," Mr. Warders said. That generous opinion was open to change.

I waited on the far side of the ravine. I figured that when the calf came squishing through the mud at the edge of the creek, I stood the best chance of getting a rope on him.

I could hear him coming along slowly and got my throwing arm ready. But I must have rustled the bushes. The calf cranked up his engine and came at top speed up the bank. I tossed the rope. The calf dipped its head. Rats! I missed.

The calf galloped by, full-speed ahead. As he passed, I lunged, grabbing him around his neck with both arms, with the sudden notion that I could break his stride and throw him.

The calf was bigger than I thought. Stronger, too. He jerked me smack off my feet. He pulled me with him as he raced along the fence; my body must have looked like coattails flying in a high wind. My boots dredged up plumes of dust behind us.

Faintly, in the distance, I could hear Mr. Warders screaming, "Turn him loose! Turn him loose!"

No way!

Finally, I got my legs stuck out in front of the calf's hooves and stiffened my knees to act as brakes. I locked down on his horns, shoving his head down toward the ground with all my strength. Instead of flopping solidly to earth as I expected, the calf's front legs folded and the rest of his body rose behind me. A shadow passed over my head. I looked up and groaned. The calf's hindquarters were coming down toward my head. We went down together with a thud, rolling in the dirt.

Suddenly, I felt my leg jerked tight against the calf's neck. The car dealer had roped us both. The calf and I scrambled to our feet at the same time. We were roped together, doing a silly dance as I tried to hold on to him while jumping around on one leg.

"You've got my leg! You've got my leg," I yelled. The calf stood still for a moment, gasping for breath—just long enough for me to yank my leg from the noose.

We were close to the Jeep. Mr. Warders flipped the other end of the rope around the front bumper and tightened it, leaving about ten feet of slack.

The blind calf went wild as soon as I got my leg free. He shot off like an arrow. The rope reeled him back in a quarter-turn arc. *Blam.* His horns smacked into the shiny Jeep's door on the driver's side. A major dent. Flecks of paint popped off.

The bull reversed quickly in the opposite direction. The rope hauled him back as he curved around the other side of the pickup. *Kablam.* He smashed into the door on the passenger's side. The calf was tattooing the Jeep's doors with his horns. I stole a look at the car dealer as I jumped toward the calf, for Warders was as furious a man as I'd seen in a month of Sundays.

"Grab that calf!" he shouted.

I already had a death grip on the horns. The calf was too tired, too addled, to keep up the good fight. He stared into space, seeing little or nothing. Mr. Warders pulled the syringe out of his jacket, yanked the top off and rammed the needle in the calf's rump.

A bone deflected his aim. The needle broke and pinged off the animal's hide. Mr. Warders' eyes followed an arc of white liquid squirting to the ground.

"Untie him," the car dealer said, his voice husky with defeat. "Let him go."

I released the dazed calf and watched him wander off in search of his path. As I got in the Jeep, I carefully avoided looking at the big dent. We didn't talk as we rocketed our way to the gate. I looked out my window at the scenery flying by, and mentally calculated the damage to the Jeep.

The next day, as I banged the posthole digger into rock-hard earth, the calf plodded by, following his accustomed routine. I didn't even stop to watch him.

About noon, a local cow trader's truck pulled up to the gate. The driver got out, dragged the gate open, closed it and rattled over.

"Where's that blind calf? Mr. Warders called my boss and said fer us to come git it. Said we could keep whatever we made off it at the sale."

I pointed in the direction the calf had gone.

"He was headed that way last time I saw him," I said. "Sorry I can't give you a hand. I've got to get this section done by evening."

Another thing I learned in Vietnam: Never volunteer.

Chapter 6

Dental Pandemonium

When Toby called to ask if I could do a little dentistry on his bear cub, I was momentarily at a loss.

"What cub?"

Knowing Toby, I was almost scared to ask.

I hadn't seen my friend from up on the mountain in quite a spell. Our paths just had not been tracking the same plot of ground recently. Was something was afoot that I didn't know about?

"You remember them two bears Uncle Bud and me brought back up here? The boar and sow that your friend Willie said was cubs, but they wasn't? Well, now they've had a cub," Toby said.

I did remember Toby's so-called Florida vacation. That was when he and his uncle braved that pack of wild and dirty swamp gals, rescued the bears and maybe saved their own male virtue by bribing their way out with a sack of peaches.

Well, apparently the bears had acclimated well to the mountains and thrived. As most everything does when Toby gets hold of it.

"Yeah law, Toby, now I've caught up with you," I said. "What's the matter with your cub's teeth? Why in the world do you want me to pull 'em?"

"Well, Doc. The cub and my dog was having a little tussle other day, and somehow I got in 'twixt the two of 'em, and that little bear sunk them fangs in my leg. It was an accident, you know, but I want you to take them fangs out. I can't barely get around for the pain of that bite. 'Course it was an accident, but I don't aim to let it happen another time."

He promised to bring the cub into the clinic the next afternoon for its dental appointment.

Before he hung up, I asked him how much the cub weighed. He replied, "Oh, 'bout 150 pounds. It's still a little thing."

Tall, raw-boned Toby *would* think along those lines. Any time we had a large animal call to his place, we could count on him to pin his animal down and make our job easier. But to my way of thinking, 150 pounds is still a right good chunk of bear.

I asked Toby if he could hold the cub down while I put it under anesthesia, and he replied without hesitation, "Sure I can." He sounded offended that I should even ask.

So when I planned that dental procedure, I counted on Toby's certainty that he was more than able to cope with his baby bear. Because we could count on that bear for no help at all.

I decided to use Treatment Room Three for the operation. You need to visualize the layout of the clinic, because logistics played a part in what happened later.

The clinic's three small-animal treatment rooms are side by side on a hallway that connects them to the waiting room. The rooms are about eight feet by nine feet, just enough space for an examining table, a chair and basic supplies and equipment needed for treatment of minor problems. Each room has two doors. One opens onto the hallway; the other, in the opposite wall, opens into the rest of the clinic. On that side are the laboratory, operating rooms, x-ray, kennel, our offices and other facilities.

Room Three has a stainless-steel, L-shaped table which serves as both scales and treatment table. The upright shaft is parallel to the wall. The short shelf rests low to the floor, making it easy to get an animal onto the shelf to be weighed. The shelf can be adjusted to hoist the patient to the right height for examination and treatment.

(Those scales gave us all a laugh one day. A portly lady brought her Pekingese in for treatment and was assigned that room. The scales had malfunctioned and were 20 pounds shy of the truth. I left the lady in there with her pet while I went out to get some medicine. When I returned, I surprised her. She was standing on the low shelf, looking at the scales' indicator on the wall behind the table. She glanced over her shoulder as I came in, smiled sheepishly, then peered closer at the indicator.

"Are these scales right, Doctor Orr?"

She had this hopeful look in her eyes. It was more than I could do to disappoint her. Besides, what could a Southern gentleman say?

"Yes ma'am! Right on the button!"

The springs *poinnggged* as she stepped off the shelf. She raised her fist, yanked it down sharply. Her voice could be heard all over the clinic as she joyously shouted, "Yesss!")

But back to Toby.

We were ready when he and the bear arrived. The "little" bear was on a leash. It snuffled uncertainly as it looked around the unfamiliar surroundings. As luck would have it, there were several dogs and cats waiting in the lobby, and more in the kennel.

Talk about pandemonium! Every dog in the clinic erupted in a howling frenzy. The hair on every cat rose as if electrified, and hisses sizzled.

It's times like this that I'm glad our clinic stands alone, with some land between it and the neighboring buildings. If ever we had a houseful of howlers and hissers, that was the day. Barely able to hear ourselves holler, Toby and I hustled the cub into Room Three.

Dental surgery on a bear is tough. The procedure is made more exciting because the injection of anesthesia is a stinging hair-raiser. One never knows what will happen before the anesthesia stops burning and shuts down the bear's brain.

Toby's cub, a roly-poly wad of dark fur, was already pretty flustered by the commotion. The strange smells and room and people didn't help. But although the cub was agitated, Toby was calm. I asked him again if he thought we needed someone to help him hold the cub down until the anesthesia took effect.

"Nah, Doc," he said. "I got it under control. Ready when you are."

With that, he tightened the leash, clasped the halter with both hands, threw one leg over the cub's shoulders, hunkered down on its back and locked the bear between his thighs.

He nodded to go ahead. The room was too tight for me to move around the bear to give the shot in its rump, so I slipped out the door to the interior of the clinic, closing the door behind me, and circled around to the other door to Room Three. I opened it quietly.

I had a fine posterior view of Toby and his cub. The two of them just about filled the small room. I stooped down, syringe in hand, pulled the cub's left rear leg out and warned the animal in my best professional bedside manner: "This is going to sting just a little."

With a quick jab, I inserted the syringe. Sure enough, it stung. The bear went ballistic. It hurled itself skyward, taking Toby with it. The cub's squeals reverberated off the walls of the cubicle. Immediately, we had an echoing uproar throughout the clinic. The bear was pawing the air, searching for something it could sink its claws and teeth into. Toby was holding the skin on the back of the bear's neck, ducking from side to side as it heaved and tossed.

If the anesthesia didn't take effect pretty quick, Toby was going to experience those teeth again. That's when this vet didn't want to get between Toby and his pet. I decided they could settle their own differences.

I knew if that bear came streaking out of the treatment room and went on a rampage through the rest of the building, we'd have disaster on our hands. I prudently stepped back, slammed the door behind me and leaned against it. I could feel the whole place shake as Toby and his bear bounced off walls, crashed into the table and against the closed doors.

I held my breath. Finally, peace descended on Room Three. I tapped on the door: "Toby? You okay?"

Silence. I tapped harder and called louder.

"Toby? You okay?"

I don't know what I'd have done if Toby hadn't answered. I knew I'd feel real bad, though.

"The booger's down. You can come on back in now," I heard him gasp.

We hauled the sleeping patient off the floor and onto the table. I jacked the table up and began to extract those murderous teeth from the bear's formidable maw.

It was some job. A bear's canine teeth, the incisors, are unbelievably long. Finesse, not brute force, is the way it has to go. Otherwise, the tooth might break off, or the jaw could be fractured. I created a flap on the bone beside each incisor, elevated the long teeth enough to ease them out sideways, then sutured the flaps of tissue over the sockets.

We carried the groggy bear to its cage in the bed of Toby's hard-used Toyota. I told Toby to keep a close eye on the cub, and to call me if he needed me.

When its jaw healed, minus the long canine teeth, the cub could chew its food with no problem. And if he did accidentally gnaw on Toby, there would probably be no loss of life or limb.

But I sure hope the next bear Toby brings in here will not need braces for a pretty smile or something. Ursine orthodontia is right down there with pigs, in my book. Never going to be my specialty.

Chapter 7

The Woman with a Heart of Gold

I had just finished surgical repairs on a dachshund that was suffering from what we call the big dog–little dog syndrome. The dachshund was the loser in a battle with a chow. His lacerations were pretty severe, but they would mend.

Marcine, the vet tech, was putting the little dog to bed in the recovery room when the crash of metal against metal froze all of us in our tracks.

For an instant, we all stopped what we were doing and listened. Then staff and clients alike raced outside, some with pets in arms.

A truck and a car had collided on the busy road in front of the clinic. Traffic in both lanes was halted bumper to bumper behind the wreck. Brakes were screeching as more drivers stopped just short of slamming into the growing jam.

Directly in front of our building, a late-model Mercedes had been knocked sideways, with its front wheels turned at an odd angle into the driveway of the clinic. The back end of the car was a crumpled mess.

Behind the Mercedes was an aged, once-green-and-cream Chevrolet pickup. Steam gushed from the radiator. The grill and bumper were mangled.

An elderly gentleman, shaking as if palsied, got out of the rusty old truck, and walked to the front of it. He held onto the fender, staring in dismay at the car he had rear-ended.

I saw the door of the Mercedes open; a woman twisted out of the driver's seat and stepped from the car. She was bent over, her hand against her chest.

"Call 911," I shouted, running toward the driver. "It looks like she's got chest injuries."

The same idea had already occurred to our technician. I saw the coattails of her surgical gown flapping as she flung open the clinic door and ran inside. Some of the staff and I hurried to help the woman from the Mercedes. To our surprise, she ignored our outstretched hands and walked on by us, her shoulders tucked in as if she were cradling her pain.

Still holding her closed left hand against her chest, the woman focused her attention on the old man. A couple of people had rushed to his aid. His wrinkled face sagged with anxiety. He was trembling. The lady stepped between the clusters of people and moved to the old man. She wrapped her right arm around the man's shaking shoulders and gave him a gentle hug.

I thought, *Dear Lord, this lady's got chest injuries, and she's hugging that poor old fellow! What a kind gesture!*

I was grateful when I heard sirens howling, way down the road. I moved toward the two drivers, worried because she was so pale and he was visibly shaking. As I drew close to them, I heard her whisper soothing words in his ear: "It's going to be all right, now. Don't you worry, you hear?"

I touched her arm, feeling like an intruder, and suggested she sit down while we helped him. She turned, paused for a second as if shifting her thoughts, and looked down at my stained scrub shirt. Only then did she move her left hand from her chest. She held out that hand to me.

For the first time, I saw wisps of black protruding from the protective curl of her fingers.

"Please take care of this for me, will you?" she asked.

Puzzled, I held out my hand. She gently put a dark bird into my palm. A chimney swift. It did not move.

"I think its wing is hurt. It hit a window at our house. I was bringing it to you when this poor man hit me," she said.

By this time, red and blue lights were flashing toward us. Two EMS ambulances, police cars and a highway patrol car arrived. The crew from one ambulance took charge of the old man. Medics from the other had brought out a stretcher and started assisting the woman. I hurried into the clinic, put the bird into an empty cage, then ran back to the parking lot.

All the while, I thought about the woman's extraordinary kindness. She must have been holding that wounded bird close to her heart as she drove to our clinic. The driver of the truck behind her apparently failed to notice that she was turning into the clinic parking lot, and rammed into her car. And yet, she was more worried about her little bird and the other driver than she was about herself or her luxury automobile.

Back outside, I saw that a small crowd had gathered. We all watched as the medics helped the two drivers.

The trooper was talking to the driver of the truck; other officers were directing traffic around the wreck when a fast-moving, low-slung sports car wheeled into the driveway. A man flung open the car door and hurried toward the ambulances. For some reason, we all concluded he was the woman's husband. The crowd turned to look at him as he rushed forward.

To our amazement, the fellow rushed right by the woman, who was being strapped onto a stretcher for a trip to the hospital. Her hand reached out tentatively, and her eyes, like ours, followed him as he strode past her stretcher. I saw her face and turned my eyes.

He did not stop. Without even looking at her, he went to the rear of the Mercedes and popped open the battered trunk lid. He pulled out a bag of golf clubs, set it on the ground and checked the clubs. Then he inspected the damage to the Mercedes, and his face puckered in a stern frown.

Finally, he hoisted the golf bag's strap onto a shoulder and, carrying his precious clubs, went to check on his wife.

A spectator next to me asked, "Did you see that? I mean, really! I don't believe it!"

I survived Vietnam, college and vet school. I've been in practice for years. I've seen human nature at its best and at its worst. Yet I still am sometimes amazed and often angered by the way some people behave.

Gritting my teeth, I said to the spectator, who kept shaking his head in disbelief, "If ever that man was going to say anything about that wrecked car, he just blew his chance."

With the crash victims inside, neither critically hurt, apparently, the ambulances pulled onto the highway, lights blinking, sirens winding up. The crowd began to disperse.

By the time the golfer had stashed his clubs in his car and driven away, I was back inside, examining the chimney swift the woman had entrusted to me.

As I held the wounded bird, I thought about the couple, and wondered what they had in common. Maybe their differences were what defined their relationship.

From the moment I saw that woman, hidden bird in hand, giving a hug to that old man, I knew we had encountered something all too rare: the gift of truly selfless love.

Sad to say, the bird had suffered fatal internal injuries when it hit the window.

We lost a chimney swift that day. But we found new wonder in the beauty of human nature. Or at least, in some of it.

Chapter 8

Granny Smith and the Coconut Cake

All weekend, a worry nagged at the back of my mind: Did the old man's cow live?

It started with a late call Saturday evening.

A man, whose quavery voice made me think he was in his seventies or eighties, asked what he should do about his Jersey milk cow.

"Bossy's bloated, Doc, and her gums are a-turnin' blue, and she's takin' little short breaths."

That was bad news: the shortness of breath told me the old man's cow was in dire straits. Something she had eaten, possibly a patch of lush clover, had fermented in the first two of the four compartments in her stomach. Or it might be that something was lodged in her esophagus, and was keeping her from belching. Cows must belch to dispel gas buildup.

Whatever the reason, the cow was filling up with methane gas. Unless the gas was released soon, that Jersey milk cow was as good as dead.

I asked where the farmer lived, ready to leave right away. When he told me he lived on Big Eastatoee, I knew we had a real crisis on our hands. He was a good hour away from the clinic, and the cow didn't have an hour to spare.

The beautiful Eastatoee Valley is one of nature's grandest places: a mountain-rimmed stretch of meadowland carved out by the clear, rocky waters of Big Eastatoee and Mill Creek. But it's remote.

I hated to tell the man that he was on his own until I got there, and that he had to do something immediately to save Bossy. "Do you have a garden hose handy?" I asked him.

"Yessir, I do."

"That's great. Now I want you to measure your cow, from her nose back to her last rib, then double that length. Take your garden hose and cut it off to match the doubled length. That will give you plenty of hose," I told him.

"Yessir, I understand. Double the length between her nose and her ribs. But then what do I do?"

"Okay, now smooth one end of the hose. Use your knife to whittle off the sharp edges. Put a piece of a two-by-four or something like that in her mouth to keep her from biting into the hose, and then carefully push the smooth end of the hose down the cow's esophagus and into the rumen, the first stomach chamber. That'll release the gas and take the pressure off right away," I told him. "Do that, and when I get there, I'll...."

He interrupted, in a hurry to get on with his task.

"Thank you, Doc. I'll go do that right now," he said.

"Wait a minute, Mister..." I said.

But before I could ask his name or get directions to his house, he had hung up.

So all weekend I worried. Bossy ought to be checked thoroughly. If she had had frothy bloat, I should have been there to dose her with a defoaming agent—something to cut down the foam in her stomach and prevent a relapse.

Because I didn't know who the man was or where he lived, there was nothing I could do. Sometimes, things just don't go the way they ought to.

Early Monday morning, I got a phone call. I recognized the old gentleman's voice.

"I want to thank you, Doc," he said. "Bossy is doing just fine. I sure do thank you."

He kept repeating his appreciation, and I told him, "You're welcome, sir. I'm sure glad she's doing fine."

Dr. Mullikin, my senior partner walked by and heard me say, "You're welcome," several more times. He waited until I hung up.

"What was that about? Who was so grateful? What was it you did?"

I told Jim the story, and realized that, once again, the man had not given me his name.

Jim teased, "Well, with such a satisfied customer, you ought to have been paid."

He laughed and went on about his business. Even though he was just fooling when he said that, I felt a twinge of guilt. I knew he was joking, but I wanted to hold up my end of the partnership.

I left the clinic to go out on a large animal call, and was away a couple of hours. When I came back, I found a perfect, big, green Granny Smith apple on my desk.

"Where did this come from?" I asked the receptionist.

"An old couple came in and said they wanted to thank you for saving their cow this weekend," she said, grinning.

I was quick to show the apple to Jim. "See! I do get paid for my work," I said. I ate the apple before Jim got his part.

The following morning, the technician and I left the clinic early on an emergency call. We struggled with a colicky horse for several hours before we finally got her some relief.

When we returned to the clinic, I parked behind the building, came in the back door and walked past the kitchen. There on the table was a lopsided coconut cake, one side about two inches higher than the other. I stepped in to see who had baked such a piece of work.

"What's that?" I asked one of the staff members who was taking a break. She shrugged, so I looked closer at the cake.

"Thanks for saving my cow."

The words, shaped from rolls of blue icing, tilted this way and that. But the message was clear, and the cake was beautiful to me.

I knew where it came from. The Eastatoee valley. I had indeed been paid. With dividends. But my benefactors never gave their names.

Sometimes, when I get a chance to go to the valley, I drive slowly past the farms and their serene old houses. And I wonder: *Is that where those good people live? And how is their cow?*

Chapter 9

Enough, Enu, Enough

Enu is a firm believer in the old saying, "What's mine is mine, and what's yours is mine, too."

Enu is my dog. He's able to live by the principle that possession is nine-tenths of the law because his ancestry is husky, chow, German Shepherd and Saint Bernard. That gives him an edge over most challengers.

Enu, pronounced *Eenew*, which is what I heard the Japanese call their dogs, is a muscular, robust 90-pounder. Generally, he is a lovable creature. He exercises great restraint, particularly around family and friends. His problems (and ours) stem from his strong, protective, possessive instincts.

Enu feels it is his duty to investigate every strange noise he hears on his property—that is, the house and farm that Betsy and I pay the taxes on—and to defend it when he perceives a threat. A threat can be a rabbit crossing the yard, a roosting guinea or a team of temperance ladies and their shopping bags of tracts.

Once, Lord help us, it was Santa Claus.

We have this friend who gets a whole year's worth of kicks by going around in a big, old, floppy Santa suit and a white beard, a floppy red cap and black boots. Thank goodness, he does this mostly just at Christmas, and mostly to take presents to people he kind of knows.

Knowing us real well did not prevent him from showing up one Christmas Eve. He came to bring a sack of toys for our little boy Ethan. Santa had lots and lots of stops to make, so he parked his Jeep down on the road, intending to walk up to the house and surprise Ethan.

In his excitement, Santa forgot about Enu.

We heard Enu's deep-throated bark, the one that means he is itching for a fight. We looked out the window, and saw a streak of red galloping down the driveway, pursued by a streak of white.

Santa hurtled out to the road and into his Jeep so fast, he wouldn't have needed a sleigh and eight tiny reindeer. He didn't even stop to wish us all a good night. What saved Santa's red rear end was the fact that he had left his driver's-side door open. We heard tires flinging gravel. Enu strolled back up the hill nonchalantly. He felt he had done a good night's work and deserved a reward.

When Santa got his nerves steadied, he drove up to the front door to visit Ethan, who was thrilled. After I assured Enu that Santa was okay, he wagged his tail and settled down to wait for a bone (if not a leg) to show up in his stocking.

Not only does Enu own the farm, but he also considers my truck his. He loves to go with me when I get an emergency call at home. As soon as he hears me come out the back door, he's at the truck, hoping this trip is his. Sometimes it takes a lot of persuasion to make him stay home.

Late one Friday afternoon, I got a call about a mare that had just given birth and was bleeding badly. I ran to the truck, in too much of a hurry to argue with Enu. He hopped in and settled down on the floorboard—his usual place on a hot day. He likes the floor vent opened so the air can ruffle his thick fur coat and cool him off.

It was muggy. The weekend had begun and traffic was heavy. It seemed everybody had places to go and wanted to get there fast. I knew the lakes nearby would be swarming with boats early Saturday morning. Casually I glanced at the gas gauge. *Dang,* and a few more words. The truck was almost out of gas.

One thing about my truck is that the gas gauge means business. When the needle touches E, you're running on fumes. I knew I couldn't get to the horse in time unless I got gas. A bread–beer–milk–gas–video poker store was around the next curve. As the convenience store came into view, I beat my fist on the steering wheel. There were cars at all the pumps, with more waiting in line. Several drivers stood around catching up on gossip.

But I had no choice. This was the only gas station for miles. I pulled in and sat there with the motor idling, fuming in frustration. Then I got an idea: If I went ahead and paid for the gas, I would be a few minutes closer to getting on my way.

Leaving Enu sleeping soundly, I jumped out of the truck and hurried inside. There were several people in front of me at the counter. I was fit to be tied. Finally, I was at the head of the line at the register. I shoved $5 in the clerk's hand and told her I'd be back to fill up later. I looked over my shoulder at the parking lot, to see if the lines were any shorter.

What I saw was surreal. My white pickup was moving slowly toward the pumps. I realized that, in my haste, I had left it out of gear.

My heart sank. The pickup was headed in the direction of a shiny, brand-new, black Cadillac, where a man was holding the nozzle at the back fender. The man glanced up. He promptly dropped the nozzle.

I saw him running toward what he thought was an empty truck. He didn't know what I knew about Enu. I almost knocked a couple of people down as I headed out the door, but before I could shout a warning, the Caddie's owner had already jerked the truck door open

and hopped in. As he landed behind the steering wheel, a white ball of fur erupted from the floorboard. The cab of the truck—the entire parking lot—resounded with Enu's fiercest get-off-my-property bark.

I was still running when I saw the man fall sideways out of the truck and land on the asphalt. He scrambled to his feet, snatched a quick look at his luxury car and jumped back to the truck. He fox-trotted beside the door; the truck was picking up speed. Then the daring, brave man rammed his arm in the window, despite Enu's snarls and snaps, and reached behind the wheel toward the gearshift.

Enu was in an uproar, trying to bite the man's arm. Just as I reached the truck, darned close to hyperventilation, the Caddie's owner yanked the gearshift upward into reverse. The truck shuddered to a stop, just inches from his car.

It's strange how a few seconds can last a lifetime. Enu calmed down immediately when he saw I was there to defend his rights. His attitude was, *Hey, I've done my job. Where were you?*

He was well-satisfied with himself. I swear there was a grin on his face as he leaned out the window, panting, his tongue dripping drool on the door.

The Cadillac owner was not smiling. His face was awash with sweat. He, too, was breathing heavily. He pulled out a bandanna and wiped his face. He still hadn't said anything. I doubt he could have.

I suddenly wanted to sit down, but this was no time for that. I looked at the man's arm. No harm done. Another reason to be grateful. Finally, when I thought I could say something coherent, I offered my hand.

"Buddy, you did a good job there." I said. "Thanks a lot. But you sure think more of that Cadillac than you do your arm."

The man still didn't speak. He didn't even shake my hand. He just turned and walked back to his car, shaking his head.

The line had thinned out. It was our turn. Enu stuck his head out the window and looked around happily as he watched me pump gas into our truck. When we were back on the road, he stretched out on the seat, put his head on my leg and slept contentedly as I drove as fast as I dared to the stable. The horse's owner was waiting in the driveway when I drove up.

"I was getting so worried. I was afraid you got lost or had run into trouble on the way," she said.

"I had to stop for gas," I said. "There was a long line."

Enu, worn out from doing his duty, slept in the truck while I doctored the mare. When she was out of danger, I checked her foal. It was healthy and hungry. The owner was as relieved as I was. It had been a close call.

I put my bag in the truck, then just sat behind the steering wheel without moving for a while. I felt as if I had run a marathon. Enu, on the other hand, woke up refreshed. He was rested after another successful sortie. He sat up on his haunches, alert, checking every move I made, grinning at the cars passing by. He nudged my arm playfully. It was all I could do to scratch his ears.

I turned back onto the main highway at the intersection and saw the gas station where Enu and I had created such a commotion. I thought about filling the tank, and decided, *No, not right now.*

Like I told him, "I've had enough today, Enu. More than enough."

71

Chapter 10

There's Stable;
Then There's Unstable

It was in a weak moment that I bought this horse.

There was a sale at Clemson University. They were selling some horses that had been in a feeding trial; the horses had not been broken to halter or saddle. But Clemson is my school, and there was this loyalty thing—and horses that needed good homes. I thought it would be nice to own one.

At that time, I lived in an apartment complex—no pets, no pasture. But here was a gift horse. Almost. How could anybody worry about trivia in the face of such an opportunity? One thing at a time here. I would work out the details when the time came.

So, sight unseen, I bought a horse by proxy.

One afternoon, with no advance warning, this wild horse was delivered in a trailer to our clinic. I had not gotten around to getting a place for her, so that mare's arrival put me in a bind.

"What am I going to do?" I asked our receptionist. "They've brought my horse and I've got no place to keep her! Any ideas?"

I was desperate. This lady had a lot of horse experience. She was cool. She said, "I know a trainer who boards horses. I imagine he would probably also take care of breaking your horse for you."

She dialed the guy's number. I waited anxiously while she explained my situation. She asked if he had a vacant stall and time to take on another client. To my relief, he said to bring the horse on over. So she went out and told the driver, who was still sitting out in the lot, with that horse getting very restless in his trailer, how to get to the trainer's stable, a few miles away. My problem was solved.

For the next few weeks, I was so busy that I couldn't take time to get out to the stable and get acquainted, either with my horse or the trainer. All I heard were messages relayed through the receptionist. All the words were encouraging.

"The horse is getting accustomed to being in close contact with people."

"The horse is getting used to a halter."

"She's handling good. The ground work is coming along fine."

"The mare is getting used to being cross-tied."

Still my horse, its trainer and I were strangers. That went against the grain. I did not want to be an absentee owner and act as though my horse was a mere possession. I wanted to get involved with the life and training of my own horse.

So, one warm afternoon when I was off duty, I decided, *Today's the day!* I didn't telephone the trainer, figuring it would be simpler to drive out to his place. I was sure he would be around the barn, or in the ring, working with one of the horses.

It was a perfect afternoon. Bright. Sunshiny. A delicious lazy Southern summer day. I drove up the dirt road to the trainer's barn. On a ridge, I could see white-painted fences surrounding a weathered barn, and pastures in half-dry grass. A summer rain would be welcome, I thought. But not today.

I parked near the fence and yelled, "Hello!" There was no response. No one was around. I walked through red dust to the barn—actually a three-stall stable with an overhang sheltering the open front. The horse boxes lined up against the back wall. The rustic building had some age on it; its walls were one-by-tens—unpainted, warped planks. It smelled richly of manure, feed, horse sweat and sawdust.

Two of the three stalls were occupied; the middle one was empty. Both horses turned their heads to watch me approach, and the sorrel mare, as much a stranger to me as I was to her, widened her eyes as I came close.

"Still feeling a little antsy around strangers, huh?" I rubbed the horse's rubbery nose, and offered her an apple I had brought. I talked to her, patted her neck and admired her clean lines. She was a beautiful horse—a solid reddish-brown coat, a blaze on her nose.

I looked at her feet. Uh-oh. Four white feet. I remembered an old saying that horse traders lived by: "Four white feet, keep him not a day. Three white feet, send him on his way. Two white feet, give him to a friend. One white foot, keep him to the end."

Bad news, if you believe old sayings. Well, it was too late now. This horse belonged to me.

She was still nervous, showing a lot of eyeball, but settling down. I decided to check out how well she responded to cross-tying. There were a couple of chains dangling from a hook nearby, so I led her out of her stall and over to a post which supported the overhanging roof of the stable. I snapped a chain to the metal ring on one side of her halter and connected the other end to an eye-bolt screwed into a one-by-ten plank on the middle stall. I hooked the other chain to the halter and attached it to an eye-bolt on the post.

The horse wasn't all that comfortable with being cross-tied by a stranger. She tossed her head nervously and stamped her feet in a skittish manner. I heard a metallic clang. I turned and saw that a chain to her halter had come loose and was slapping against the post.

The sound frightened her. She reared. Her white feet pawed the dusty air. As she came down, she backed away from me. As she reversed at full speed, her weight took all the slack out of the crosstie that was hooked to the post. I heard an awful sound.

Yyyyerrrerk.

The eye-bolt on the middle stall's plank gave way. She jumped in another direction. Another *yyyyerrrerk.* Another nail screeched and came out. The plank peeled back as she lurched.

She went berserk. The hinges on the door, to which the plank was connected, ripped off, bringing down the door and another plank. The screech of nails, and the crackle of shattering wood, maddened my poor, terrified horse.

Despite my best efforts to calm her, she reared, jerking one of the stall's roof-supporting posts loose. Her great white eyes were rolling wildly. She spotted the corral and the pastures, and undoubtedly remembered the time, only a short while ago, when open spaces were the only home and security she knew or wanted.

She galloped home, dragging a 12-foot plank, the door attached to it and two more 12-foot planks, which were nailed to the door. The loose lumber, now on its way out to the corral, had been vital to the structure of the stable. The roof dropped about two feet, dust rising as the whole stable shifted, sliding slowly off its foundations.

It looked as if the barn was coming down, but I couldn't deal with that problem just then. I was running after my horse, scared to death that she was going to get tangled with the planks, posts and rusty nails she was hauling with her in her flight.

At a corner of the fence, she was penned just long enough for me to catch up. I grabbed her halter and the chain that connected her to a sizable portion of the stable's framework.

I finally got her calmed down, pulled the stall door, the planks and hinges from around her white feet, and led her back into the stable—what was left of it. It seemed to have settled safely enough. I put her in her stall and propped a dismantled door up so she couldn't get out. Then I checked on the other horse.

He spooked at the sight of me, dancing in his stall, as I got close.

"Hey, don't blame me," I told him. "It wasn't me that tore your stable up."

Just then, I heard a car droning up the dirt road. With my luck, it was bound to be the trainer. I glanced around the stable, tilting precariously on its foundation. The warm day suddenly seemed chilly. I walked out of the shambles, bending my head to keep from hitting the lowered roof.

The driver wore a Western hat that shielded his face. I could see as he got out of the car that he was a sturdy, muscular fellow, the kind of guy who would be pretty hard to flap. That was good.

He looked at the stable with a puzzled expression as he walked toward me. I told myself I had to put the best possible spin on this. *Direct action, that's the ticket,* I thought. I knew that if this guy wasn't cool-headed, I was in for a fight.

I marched up, raised my hand friendly-like and said, "Hi! I'm Doctor Orr and I just destroyed your stable."

His expression did not change. He didn't say anything, just walked past me to what was left of the stable. He was stone-faced. I followed him as he tromped slowly around the barn inspecting the wreckage. I kept quiet, not wanting to do or say anything that would set off an explosion.

Man, say something! Anything! I thought. *If he decides to, he can beat the pulp out of me. He'll blow up any minute, now, and I'll have to fight him to try to save my skin.*

Finally, after a silence so thick I could slice it, the trainer cleared his throat and said quietly, "Well, I guess you're as welcome out here as I am."

I spent the rest of the day with that understanding, kind, wonderful man. We rebuilt his stable together. I knew that a man of such patience would be a good trainer for my mare.

The sorrel with four white feet turned out to be a good little horse. I sold her the minute I could.

Chapter 11

The Diagnosis

Billy and Jennie McJimpsey Orr had four sons: Jim, Mickey, Wayne and me. We were blessed with the freedom of country-raising on Daddy's dairy farm in Oconee County, and we were a handful. "Reliable witnesses" remind us so, to this very day.

A Canadian of Scotch-Irish heritage, our mother grew up in Vancouver, where her father and brothers were lumbermen, as were all their neighbors.

When she was in a mood to remember, Mama talked occasionally about the days of her childhood. I get a cold spot in my heart when I recall her stories about how the family existed on smoked salmon in Vancouver's frozen winters.

"We ate it for breakfast. We ate it for lunch. We ate it for supper," she told us. "But there's one thing about dried salmon. If you could chew it, and if you could swallow it, it killed the hunger."

The unscheduled shriek of the lumber mill's steam whistle filled Mama's childhood with horror.

"When the steam whistle blew," she said, her voice solemn, "we knew that someone had died in an accident. For the rest of the day we waited, worrying and wondering. Was it our daddy? Our brothers? It was not until along about dusk that we could look down the long road and, in the distance, see our family coming home. We counted their heads as they came over the hill. Only then did we know they were safe. This time."

Her words painted in my mind a vivid picture of the anxiety she and her mother and sisters suffered. I could see her standing in the last light of day, watching her daddy and brothers coming home. I experienced the relief she felt when everyone was accounted for.

As a young girl, Mama dreamed of a career in medicine and had already enrolled in medical school when World War II broke out. She didn't hesitate. She became a nurse on a military hospital ship, taking care of soldiers wounded in the major theaters of the war. Isn't it strange that military jargon refers to bloody battlefields as "theaters"? As if war were a stage. I hate what war does to people.

Yet, without the war, Billy Orr and Jennie McJimpsey never would have met. She was the nurse assigned to take care of him after he was injured in battle. They fell in love, married and came to Walhalla to raise cattle and children in Billy Orr's part of the world. Mama continued to work as a nurse while raising us boys. We were the core of her life.

We were hardy kids. I don't remember being sick but once, and that was when I went swimming in a cow pond and got an infection in my ears. The doctor prescribed penicillin. He gave Mama a vial of the antibiotic so she could give me the shots I needed. She lured me up close by holding out a sucker, while hiding the needle behind her back. When I jumped within arm's reach—*pow!* I paid for those suckers with shots in the rump. You'd think I would have caught on, but her trick worked every time. Suckers were hard to come by in those days.

I don't remember, as a kid, actually telling anybody that I was going to be a vet when I grew up. (There were times, I imagine, when people who knew me doubted I would grow up, yet I surprised them and myself.) But I do remember thinking that Dr. Kellett was a magician.

Dr. Kellett took care of my daddy's cows. When a cow went down with milk fever, Daddy called Dr. Kellett. The cow would be stretched out as if she were ready to die the next minute. The vet hung an IV and got some fluid in her. Within moments, she scrambled to her feet and started eating, as if nothing had happened. It was a miracle.

I was a second-grader when I laid claim to a calf soon after its birth. I loved that little creature; I liked the feel of her velvet muzzle when I fed her from my hand, and her coat was pure silk. The calf grew up and became part of the milking herd, but she was still my cow. Then she got sick and Daddy had to call Dr. Kellett. I was mighty worried. Daddy didn't want me around when the vet arrived, so I knew he thought something was bad wrong with my cow.

When Daddy and Dr. Kellett went into the barn, I crawled on my hands and knees along the outside until I found a crack where I could see inside the barn. I watched everything Dr. Kellett did and listened to every word he said. I heard him tell my father something about "the diagnosis." My heart started pounding.

I had heard Daddy tell of a cow having "ketosis," but "diagnosis"—that was a new and terrifying word to my ears. It started with "die." I ran crying to the house. Dad had been right! It was bad!

"Mama! Mama!" I wailed as I ran in the kitchen. "My cow's got diagnosis! She's got diagnosis!" I was yelling and crying at the same time.

Mama broke into laughter, then grabbed me in a tight hug and explained the meaning of the word "diagnosis." I listened and stopped crying. Mama raised us with wisdom and love. She had a way with words, with the ability to cut to the heart of the matter, and she knew how to be gentle.

The terrible day came, much too soon, when she had to explain her own diagnosis to her grown-up boys. It was cancer.

Chapter 12

A Matter of Degrees

Long before Vietnam altered my life—before Tri-County Tech, or Clemson, or Tuskegee, or the practice of veterinary medicine—I was a high school student, barely skimming by.

My parents moved us from Walhalla to Greenville. I had loved growing up with the freedom of the country, and I despised crowds and city concrete. Entering the new school as a junior, I knew no one except my brothers. I paid little attention to my teachers. I learned the bare minimum and no more. I was shy and angry. I carried a chip of resentment on my shoulder the size of a four-by-four block of green oak, and I didn't willingly speak to anyone in school for six months.

I hated school.

But one of my teachers came to my rescue. Mr. Greene said he needed help on his farm a few miles out of town. My brothers and I jumped at his offer. Two of us moved out to Mr. Greene's farm. I wasn't back home, but at least I was in the country. Working on the farm made it possible for me to endure high school. I squeaked by, but I did graduate, thanks to the hogs, the hay fields and the friendship of my benefactors, Jack and Joyce Greene.

Mrs. Greene was my teacher, too, but not in a classroom. She taught me a lot about living, and helped draw me from my shell. She listened when I wanted to talk. My teenage rebellion didn't faze experienced teachers like Joyce and Jack Greene. They got me through high school. Then the U.S. Navy got a crack at me.

At age twenty-two, I returned from the wretched war in Vietnam with as many unresolved conflicts as those present in the war zone. It was 1970. After my discharge, I stood in the airport in Seattle, Washington, caught in a dilemma. I had just enough money to buy one ticket. Travelers swirled around me as I deliberated whether to return to Yokohama, Japan, and the easy money I knew could be made in the Orient in the aftermath of the bloody war, or to go home to my family and an uncertain future.

I figured life in the fast lane in Yokohama would be exciting, but risky, maybe even short. In contrast, the lifestyle back home would be slow and, to a twenty-two-year-old, boring. But I would live longer. I weighed one option against the other, and the scales tilted. I boarded a plane that returned me to the South Carolina mountains, where I belonged, drawn back by the indelible ethics and values instilled in me by my parents many years before.

Back home, I looked up my friend Mike Oliver. Mike and I had grown up within a quarter mile of each other near Walhalla. We had been buddies from childhood, even though I was four years older than he. Mike had entered high school the year I joined the Navy.

Now, Mike was ready to go to Clemson University in the fall. And I was ready to explode.

At the same time, though, I was building a determination to go to college, too. The transition was not to be an easy one.

A guidance counselor at the technical college near my old home brought me face-to-face with the future. I presented myself to Tri-County Tech to see what courses the college had to offer a Vietnam vet. Ms. Jones, the counselor, proceeded to fire off a battery of tests at me almost as frightening as a Viet Cong bombardment. When she was through evaluating my academic achievement, intelligence quotient, dexterity, career inclinations and aspirations, she knew more about me than I did.

"You're college material," she said, "but...."

I had learned early in life that "but" meant bad news. I waited with dread as Ms. Jones continued.

"You've got to start over on several subjects, some as far back as the eighth grade level. You'll be on a self-paced track. You'll go at your own speed and you'll have to cram a lot into your brain in a short time, then take the exams."

"But...but...but..." I wanted to shout. "I've seen the world! I've seen my buddies die! I've wasted four years of my life! And you're saying I've got to go back to junior high stuff? What do you think I am?"

But I didn't say it aloud. I just watched her, as she sat quietly at her desk, watching me. "Battle ax" was the nicest of the names than ran through my mind.

Then she told me something I had heard a thousand times from my mother: My future was in my hands—

the opportunities were there, provided I was willing to reach out and grab them.

There it was again—Mama's motto: "A man's grasp should exceed his reach, or what's a heaven for?" Mama had a bagful of short sermons she shared with my brothers and me.

Now Ms. Jones was echoing Mama: "It's up to you."

The guidance counselor turned her attention to paper work on her desk as I pondered my options. She made it clear she had time to wait.

I cleared my throat and said, "Okay. What do I do? When do I start?"

She laid out the plan of action I would follow. She scheduled my courses in the college prep track without a quiver. She acted as if she thought I could do the work. Ms. Jones then dropped another bomb: "Oh, by the way, you'll have to make at least 95 on every test if you are to advance."

Throughout the summer, I pored over books, studying as I had never studied before. That mind-boggling season, I absorbed a mountain of information that I should have learned years before.

I passed the exams. Then Ms. Jones handed me over to the dean of admissions at Clemson University and he, too, proved to be a gate-opener.

As for Ms. Jones, she was no "battle-ax." Instead, she became an esteemed and cherished friend.

In Clemson, majoring in zoology, I was committed to becoming a veterinarian. Fortunately, when Mike and I graduated, Tuskegee University, in Alabama, had a reciprocal agreement with South Carolina to accept a limited number of applicants into Tuskegee's vet school.

Mike and I met the university's criteria. We spent the next four years together at Tuskegee, devouring everything we could learn from our professors.

Throughout high school, neither my parents nor the Greenes questioned me about my grades. Later, I would have loved to brag a little to them about the good grades I earned because I had finally learned to study. But I didn't; it was personal. Sure, it was their goal, too. But I had to carry the ball. Somehow, it seemed that to brag would be to fumble, and I didn't want to fumble any more. I had to prove something to myself.

I freely admit to the anger that frequently beset me in my earlier years. But now, when I think of those years, it isn't with hostility. I think of people I loved. Friends. Mama and Daddy...my brothers, our family. The Greenes. Ms. Jones. My 'Nam pals. Certain professors and administrators at Clemson and Tuskegee. Classmates.

There was one other: Dr. Kellett, the country veterinarian of my youth in Walhalla. He had a profound effect on many, but especially on two little Oconee County boys: Mike Oliver and me. More than once, we had watched the good doctor perform what we considered miracles.

When Mike and I joyously marched out of Tuskegee, with those D.V.M. certificates in our hands, we remembered Doc Kellett.

We were ready to work miracles.

Chapter 13

All That Glitters and More

Sometimes it looks like confusion makes the world go around. Nothing is exactly what it seems; embarrassment lurks like potholes in what we only *thought* was the right track.

It is good to know that error is sometimes a trial for other folks, too. A friend of mine just passed along a story. The subject is a grand, straight-spined lady who was already driving like a mad woman when the A-Model Ford was a cool new car. She would be as mad as a wet hen if she knew anybody was telling on her. So remember, you never heard a word of it from me.

This lady has lived a pretty good life without putting much dependence in the medical profession. She does not run to the doctor, and this has kind of worried her daughter, who is of a different mind.

The daughter nagged and wheedled, and finally the old lady said, Oh, all right, she would go for a pap smear, the routine maintenance checks and that sort of thing. "I'll go," she said, "but you'll have to ride over to Greenville with me."

That in itself was scary enough. The lady cherishes a distinctive car that's about as old as she is; she drives like there's not another soul on the road. Dead center in the highway, off she and the quaking daughter go to Greenville. Well, the nurse comes out and escorts Mother into the examining room. After a little bit, Mother is out again—scowling and ready for a fight.

"Mother! What's wrong?" the daughter says. "Did the doctor find something...?"

"He found the nerve to insult me!" says the old lady. "I have never been so insulted in all my life!"

"Whatever did he do?" says the daughter.

"Well," says Mother, sputtering and fuming, "there I was, on his old table, butt-naked, with my feet up in those old stirrups, and he comes in and flips back the sheet. He looks at me and smirks, and he says, 'My, aren't we fancy today!'

"I wanted to kick him!"

The daughter is puzzled. She says, "Why would he say such a thing? Did you have on something...?"

And Mother says, "I had on absolutely nothing, only the powder I put on myself every day!"

Something is wrong with this, Daughter is thinking. "Mother," she says, "maybe we ought to look...."

They go in the bathroom, and Mother takes down her panties. What comes to light sure is fancy. Mother has been working on a craft project for the church. Something that is decorated with gold glitter. Mother left the box of glitter in the bathroom. It is the same shape as Mother's bath powder. She powdered real good; no floozie in a peep show ever glittered like Mother, down below.

Mother is now having more kindly thoughts about that doctor. My friend says she asked him, "Do you think I ought to write the doctor a note and explain to him what happened?"

And the informant says he thought about it. And then he told her, "No ma'am, I believe I'd just let well enough alone...."

Human nature is full of little warps and complications.

One of the quirks across our countryside is in the way that people tend to describe a creature's ailment. People get real tense when they start talking about animal parts. They get real scientific. Take the case of a lady who called with a serious worry about her dog.

"Doctor, he's all swole up."

"Where's the swelling, Miss Myrtie?"

"Hit's back there."

"Where back there?"

"You know. Back there."

"You mean his tail?"

"No, not his tail. Hit's...his...tentacles."

A farmer called to say his cow was about to go into labor. I said, "How can you tell?"

And he said, "Well, for the last two days her rectum has been pulsorating."

Another old guy asked for a house call for his cow. He walked with me out to the barn, telling me her symptoms in some pretty high-falutin' terms.

"You know, she had a calf several days ago," he said. "And she is still bleeding from her virginia."

I agreed it sounded serious. "That's mighty dangerous territory," I said.

*　*　*

The truth is, my own glass house is way too thin for me to be throwing rocks at the slip-ups of other folks. My ears still get red when I think of a certain incident.

A woman who had not been in before brought her sick dog to the clinic. She was a beautiful blonde. Maybe it's not politically correct to notice—but there was no way not to notice this lady. I mean, she was a knockout.

I took the little dog into the treatment room, examined it, and fixed up some pills for it. When I handed the woman the bottle, I said, "Give him one of these every night, before we go to bed...."

No, she didn't hit me. She didn't sue. She gave me a big smile, and a wink. And we haven't seen her since.

Sometimes, even a little misinterpretation can be big trouble. If only I had remembered Shoki's name from his puppy chart, I might not have nearly strangled that dog. On the other hand, maybe I would have.

When the guy first brought this half-grown black puppy to the clinic, you could tell right away that the man had had no interaction with that little dog at all.

We went into one of the rooms, and the guy put the dog up on the table. It jumped down and ran off. It was not trained. When we were trying to catch it, he was calling it by some name I didn't get; the dog didn't get it, either. It was not used to coming when it was called by name—or by anything else, for that matter. So it just ran round and round through the clinic, in one room and out another, 'til finally we cornered it and gave it its shots.

Well, the next time that dog came in, I went in the treatment room, and there he was, up on the table. As

I was coming in, the owner was going out. He was this great big guy, about six-foot-four, and as he went off down the hall, he was saying, "I can't stand to see my dog get shots!"

So here I was with this dog, and he wasn't a little puppy anymore. He was a big, slick, beautiful Doberman. *Big.* I could tell right then that he wasn't socialized like he should be. He gave me a look. He was saying something disrespectful way down deep in his throat: "Hhhrrrrr...HHHRRrrrrr...."

Well, everybody on the staff was busy, and there was nobody right at hand to help me. And by then, the dog was getting pretty excited. He was looking at me, curling up his lip and showing all his big teeth, going, "HHHRRrrrr...."

I froze. Then I slowly extended my left hand, reaching for lead line. And the dog lunged. He sailed off of that table, right into my face. I ducked. His jaws barely missed my arm. As I went backward against the wall, by reflex I caught him around the neck. Adrenaline was working—mine and his. I held on, yelling for dear life. "Help! Help!" While I was yelling, I was holding 100 pounds of fighting dog, suspended in mid-air. And the dog was screaming, too. It was deafening.

The man heard all the racket and came running. The next thing I knew, he was towering over me, yelling, "Shoki! Shoki!"

I thought he was saying, "Choke 'im! Choke 'im!"

And I thought, *He wants me to train* this *dog?*

Chapter 14

Con Masters

The folks in the country where I grew up were not, for the most part, what you'd call persuasive talkers. Their conversations were mostly about family, friends, the weather, crops, or how things were going at the mill or on their farms. Shooting the bull was something a local guy did only if the brute was goring his best friend, or if it butted his new truck, or looked unkindly at his dog.

But then I got to know Silver-Tongued Tyrone.

Tyrone was a fellow student at Tuskegee, and for a while, he stood alone as the Number One Champion Bull Shooter.

Silver-Tongued Tyrone had the ability to dazzle even our professors with his brilliant orations. He would strike a pose of authority beside an animal's carcass in pathology lab and deliver an eloquent monologue about the animal's pathophysiology. Never mind that it was a mish-mash of words gleaned from random readings in veterinary medicine textbooks. Whatever he said sounded great. Students who didn't know better thought he was a genius talking gospel. They took notes when Tyrone talked.

The professors were awed, too, but in a different way. They were impressed, not with Tyrone's knowledge, but with how smoothly the meaningless jargon rolled off Tyrone's silver tongue. I used to enjoy watching them roll their eyes at one another when Tyrone launched himself to new heights of grandiloquence.

There was a time, though, when Tyrone's spiel failed him, and he was unable to con his way out of a situation. That day, it was his misfortune to be walking across campus, on his way to lunch, when he was collared by Dr. Blackwell, the professor of ambulatory care, who was leaving campus on a farm call.

Dr. Blackwell, who also served as a vet to farmers who lived near the college, always grabbed as many of his students as he could when he went on a call. He believed that every call offered opportunities to apply what we were learning in the classroom. Trips with Dr. B were like pop quizzes in which he tested our newly acquired knowledge.

But on this occasion, he came up short. Not one of his students was within sight in the building. He stepped outside and spotted Tyrone double-stepping his way toward the dining hall.

"Come with me. I've got to check on a cow in labor," Dr. B commanded.

"I'm on my way to lunch. I'm hungry, Dr. Blackwell. Get someone else this time," Tyrone said. "Please."

Dr. B insisted. Tyrone resisted.

"I'm starving. I haven't eaten all day," Tyrone moaned, but Dr. B was adamant. The two of them left campus in Dr. B's pickup, one satisfied with the outcome of the debate, the other pouting.

As we followed him around while he treated farmers' animals, Dr. Blackwell lectured to us about situations he had encountered and offered us practical suggestions, based on his experiences. One piece of advice he passed along was "How To Make a Clean Get-Away When the Situation Arises."

He said, "Always leave the door of your vehicle open when you make your first visit. You never know what awaits. A vicious dog, for instance. So leave the door open." We dutifully tucked that word of wisdom among our overflowing brain cells.

On this call with his reluctant companion, Tyrone, Dr. B took his own advice. This was a first-time visit to this farmer's place, so he left the truck door open and told Tyrone to wait until he checked things out. Dr. B walked toward the house, calling, "Hello! Hello! Anyone home?"

There was no answer. He walked up a flight of steps, knocked on the door, and called out again.

This time he got a response: a sleek Doberman pranced around a corner of the house and greeted him with bared teeth. Dr. B saw the snarling dog, took a flying leap off the porch, and raced toward the truck, thankful that he had remembered his own advice. About ten feet from his truck, to his horror, he saw the door closing.

Tyrone's teeth gleamed in a sweet smile. He reached over and locked the door as Dr. B made a desperate lunge. The professor had limited choices. The bed of the truck was full of vet gear, so he jumped on the hood, feeling the hot breath of the Doberman on his ankles.

The dog had four coiled springs for legs. It continued to leap about the truck with mighty bounds, gnashing its teeth. Seeking higher protection than the hood's flimsy thin metal, the professor scrambled to the roof of the cab.

The professor said later that the indignity of retreating from the guard dog did not bother him half so much as listening to Tyrone's peals of laughter. "It just didn't look professional for me to be up there on the top of the truck, waiting for rescue," he said.

Tyrone's account of their adventure was a tale of sweet revenge, beautifully told with great embellishments, of course.

But Silver-Tongued Tyrone could not hold a candle to my friend Henry.

Henry came to work as an assistant at an emergency clinic in Greenville where I started practice. He and I became good friends. He had not been with us long before his agile tongue and quick thinking were tested and found exceptional.

I had gone home one day, leaving another vet, a receptionist, and Henry on duty. I had not been home more than 30 minutes when the phone rang. It was Henry.

"Doc, there's a man out in the lobby, and he's raising all kinds of hell. It's about a bill. Doc, he's huge. The biggest man I've ever seen. Doc, he had to duck to get in the door," Henry said, talking a mile a minute.

"You know the window at the receptionist's desk, Doc? You know how high it is? Well, this man's so tall that he had to bend way down to look in."

In the background, on Henry's end of the line, I could hear deep bass rumblings and crackles like thunder, followed by the higher, tenor voice of the vet in charge. The battle of words was at fever pitch.

"Doc, do you hear that fellow?" Henry asked, speaking furtively into the phone. "He leaned down in the receptionist's face and shouted: 'Somebody's gonna pay!' Scared her to death."

"So?" I asked Henry. "What's the problem? You're in charge. Handle it. Throw the jerk out!"

I hung up the phone and counted...one, two, three.

Brrng.

I knew it was Henry again. I didn't give him a chance to say a word. "Henry, I told you that you were in charge."

Henry was quiet for a second. Then he said, "Okay."

The phone dropped on its hook. I got no more calls. Not from Henry, nor from the police. The next morning, the receptionist told me what happened.

"This guy was massive, and he was mad," she said. "The reason was that, a while back, a car hit his dog, and a some thoughtful soul brought it to us. We found the owner by checking records of the dog's rabies tag. We called this guy—the one who came in mad—and he authorized us to operate on the animal. Then he picked his dog up, but he never paid his bill. It finally went to the collection agency."

She said the agency failed to collect the overdue money and listed the guy as a credit risk. The day before our debtor showed up at the clinic, he had tried to buy a mobile home, and the bank turned him down. His unpaid bill at the clinic had caught up with him.

"Boy, he was furious," she said. "But Henry was cool. He talked until he got the man calmed down."

"Did he talk the man into paying his bill?" I asked.

"Of course," she said. "When he came in, he hollered at me that 'somebody was going to pay.' After Henry talked to him, the big man paid."

I wasn't surprised. I knew something about Henry's background. He and I shared a mutual hatred of the military, only Henry's was higher, deeper and wider than mine.

Henry did not take to military life well. He would have been court-martialed if he hadn't caused so much trouble to the military judicial system. He went to the library of the base where he was stationed and consumed every book available on the laws governing military courts, making dessert of the fine print. Armed with the facts and a sense of mission, Henry used the legal system to tie up so much personnel and time in handling his case that the U.S. Army surrendered to Henry. They sent him back to Fort Jackson, South Carolina, to be discharged.

On his last day as a soldier, Henry went off base, had a few drinks in Columbia to celebrate his new freedom, and returned to the base for one last sortie against military bureaucracy.

He marched to the induction center, where a sergeant was talking to a group of recruits. Henry, who is part Indian, was dressed in civilian clothes, but he has an air of authority, and he knows how to use it.

"Sergeant," he ordered, "you're dismissed. I'll take over now."

"Who are you?" the sergeant asked.

"I'm Major Marchbanks, Sergeant." Henry lied.

But the sergeant, never one to challenge a person with authority, turned on his heel and did as the "major" ordered.

Henry strolled to the front of the room. He looked with pity on the room filled with teen-age boys. They had just stumbled off the buses which had gathered them up from cities, towns and back-country crossroads and dumped them in the sandy hell of a Southern boot camp. They were scared to death. Many were away from home for the first time, facing the Great Unknown with a mixture of fear and anticipation.

"Men," Henry told his captive audience, "this is my last day in the military, and I want to give all of you one last chance to change your minds. If any of you want to get out, now's the time. You just follow me off this base. I'm leaving today."

Half of the recruits marched out the door with Henry.

Chapter 15

Daiquiri

Mike Oliver and I were roommates the four years we spent in vet school in Alabama, where our classmates nicknamed us "Frick and Frack." The first six months at Tuskegee, we stayed in a basement apartment, where we listened to rats romping at night across the ceiling above us. As soon as we could, we moved to a trailer on a farm.

We divided household labor without a hitch. We didn't do a lot of cleaning; my job was to cook the meals, his was to wash the dishes. He studied while I cooked. Spaghetti was my specialty. He sat down to eat when the food was on the table. After polishing off a second man-sized helping, he would shove the plate to the center of the table and complain, "This stuff is not any good." It was funny. I was sure if he ate another bite, he'd explode.

When I finished eating, I left the table and studied, while Mike washed the dishes and cleaned the kitchen, more or less.

The grand day came when we were officially entitled to write D.V.M. after our names. We packed our belongings and locked the door to the rented trailer, anticipating our return to South Carolina to save the animal kingdom.

Mike closed the tailgate on his truck, walked a few steps toward the door and stopped.

"Jerry, I got to tell you something."

I braced myself for something sentimental. I mean, after all those years together, it was a significant moment. We were going to new jobs, starting our careers. Our roads of life were about to take separate paths. I waited, dreading an awkward emotional farewell to our shared past.

"What?" I asked cautiously.

"Jerry, you can't cook worth a damn," he said.

Mike began his practice with Dr. Mullikin in Easley (where I later became a partner after Mike went into practice in Seneca), and I started work at the emergency hospital for animals in Greenville. On weekends, I helped out at the Easley clinic.

At that time, Dr. Mullikin had a receptionist, a nice young lady, who took words literally—as Mike discovered for himself, thanks to Daiquiri.

Daiquiri was a cranky cat owned by Marcine, one of Dr. Mullikin's veterinary assistants. Marcine kept her old cat at the clinic, where he had the run of the place. Daiquiri added spice to his life by teasing the dogs in the kennel. He would slink by the wire cages, trolling for victims. When he spotted a dog's nose within reach, Daiquiri would hook his claws into the nostrils of the unsuspecting dog, then retreat, leaving his victim howling.

One day, the cat met his match.

In one of the cages was the clinic's blood donor, a pit bull, wise with the fullness of years. One afternoon, Donor was sprawled in his cage, watching Daiquiri enjoy a game of "let's torment the dogs." The pit bull's eyes drooped sleepily, as if he was ready for a snooze. Daiquiri decided it was time to teach the old dog a new trick. The cat's flashing claws darted into the dog's cage.

Surprise! A pair of powerful jaws locked down on the cat's paw. Donor's brain beamed his mighty jaws a message: *Don't let go! Hang in there! Keep up the good work!*

Daiquiri screeched in agony and frustration. He hung in mid-air, screaming that he was innocent. Donor had heard that excuse before. He held on.

Mike was nearby and leapt to Daiquiri's defense, but his options were limited because of the wire mesh on the cage. Somehow, Mike knew he had to make the pit bull open its jaws—quickly. Knowing he couldn't physically pry the dog's mouth open, Mike opened the door, grabbed Donor's head, and pushed it down against the mesh floor of the cage, so it would not keep pulling on Daiquiri's leg and cause more damage. He couldn't use a stick to open Donor's mouth, either, so he thought of another option.

Mike figured if he could squirt water in the dog's mouth, Donor would start choking and release Daiquiri.

Maudie, the receptionist, had dashed into the kennel to see what the uproar was about.

"Give me the hose!" Mike yelled at her as he strained to keep a grip on Donor's head. "Give it to me! Quick!"

Maudie did exactly what Dr. Oliver told her to do. She gave it to him.

She grabbed the hose from the sink, turned the faucet on full blast, aimed the hose at Mike and....Boy! Did she give it to him!

Sssspreesh! Cold water soused him. Maudie soaked Mike, the cat, the dog—the entire kennel. The animals in the cages raised their voices in harmony with Daiquiri's solo of sharp protest.

It was a moment to remember. We all laughed.

Well, most of us laughed.

Mike and Daiquiri pouted a while.

Chapter 16

Baggy Britches

Whoever said "clothes make the man," never saw Mike Oliver.

When we were in veterinary school together, Mike and I, like a lot of our classmates, envisioned ourselves eventually becoming large animal doctors. Many of the large animal doctors we came in contact with wore khaki coveralls on farm calls, both for comfort and to protect their clothing. We selected khaki coveralls as our farm call uniform, too.

Mike has big shoulders, but he's got thin shanks. When he purchases khakis big enough to go over his shoulders comfortably, there's always more than enough room in the rump. Consequently, his baggy britches seem to take on a life of their own. As he walks, he looks like a big tent with its side flaps billowing in the breeze.

Between our junior and senior years at Tuskegee, Mike and I and our classmates got summer jobs in nearby towns—Mike with a large animal veterinarian in Seneca, in Oconee County, not far from where he and I grew up together, and I at the emergency animal hospital in Greenville, about a hour's drive from Seneca. We stayed in touch, because I went over to see my father and other relatives—and Mike, of course—in Oconee as often as I could.

That summer, his baggy coveralls got him in trouble, not once, but twice. One sweltering day he made a farm call to check on a herd of Holsteins. The farmer wanted to know how many of his cows were carrying calves. When Mike arrived at the barn, he took his shirt off and put the khakis on over his jeans, leaving the uniform unzipped to his waist to keep cool.

It was milking time. The barn was filled with big Holsteins, standing patiently in metal stanchions on both sides of the barn. Electric milkers stripped their swollen udders as they munched grain.

Mike finished palpating the uterus of a cow, noting that the artificial insemination had settled and she was pregnant. He slapped her rump and stepped backward into the hallway so she could back out of her stall. He was deep in thought and paid no attention to what was going on around him. He and the cow waltzed backward together, unaware that a dramatic moment awaited them.

One of the dairy workers had disconnected the electric milkers from the cow in the stall behind Mike. That cow backed into the hall at the same moment Mike did. Her rear end collided with Mike's rear end, knocking him forward against the hind quarters of the cow he had released.

Mike discovered with a jolt that he was sandwiched between the tails of two Holsteins. Twisting frantically to extricate himself from between two bellowing cows, Mike only added to their excitement.

The cow in front reacted first. She started relieving her bowel—right down the front of his unzipped coveralls. Mike leaped in alarm. That further excited the Holstein behind him. She began filling his rear pockets—dloop, dloop, dloop.

Everybody in the barn was in tears, but no one laughed harder than Mike as he hosed himself off.

The following fall, when we returned to the campus, Mike's "full-pockets" story was one of the show-stoppers when the Tuskegee vet interns shared tales about "how I spent my summer."

I loved telling a different story about how Mike ran into trouble with his khakis at another farm, where I was witness to the events.

On one of my days off, while en route to visit my dad, I saw Mike's truck barreling down the highway toward Walhalla. I flagged Mike down, made a 180-degree turn over the median and pulled up behind him on the shoulder of the road. He said he was on his way to see about a cow that had collapsed in a creek and couldn't get back onto her feet. We both knew that if she stayed down, she would die.

I volunteered to ride along with him, and lend a hand if he needed it.

We drove up to a drought-stricken farm and met the farmer in his back lot. The three of us hiked through parched pastures to the creek. We noticed a cow on a ridge. We could see nearly every bone in her body. The farmer, striding along with us, pointed to the bag of bones and explained, "She's thin, Doc, but she ain't perishing."

A short time later, we stood beside the fallen cow lying on her side in the water. She had struggled 'til the edges of the creek were mush and the water trickling around her was orange with mud. She was almost exhausted.

"She's nearly starved," Mike said, as he stooped beside her and ran his hands over her gaunt rib cage. "A classic case of high-trough syndrome."

He was speaking to me, one professional to another. The farmer looked at us, bewildered.

"It's a term us vets use to say the trough is too high for the cow to reach the feed," I explained to the farmer, while Mike concentrated on the cow. The farmer didn't didn't smile at the small joke.

"The drought's dried up just about every blade of grass in the pasture," he said. "We sure could use a good rain hereabouts." He looked upward at the heat-bleached sky as if silently offering another in a long chain of prayers. Like his cattle, his farm was close to perishing.

Mike worked diligently with the cow, wallowing around with her in the mud until he got good and wet. He administered bottles of glucose and electrolytes, trying to pump in enough energizing fluid to revive her, but she still couldn't get to her feet.

"She's just too weak from lack of groceries," he said.

He had brought along the "hot stick" with his instruments. The battery-operated device looks like a small flashlight with two probes sticking out. This electric prod sometimes is the only thing that will get results when you want stubborn cattle to move.

Mike tried the "hot stick" after all other solutions failed. The cow trembled slightly as a low volt of electricity surged into her, but she still didn't get up. Her spirit seemed willing, but her poor, frail body was just too weak.

Mike stood up, studying his patient, trying to figure out something else. Without thinking, he shoved the "hot stick" into a back pocket of his wet khakis. I figured he was getting ready to ask me to help shove her on her chest so we could manhandle her to her feet; but he didn't say anything, so I waited. It was his case. He squatted down beside the cow in the creek.

Zzzt! Zzzt! Zzzt!

I heard the "hot stick" in his pocket go off and realized that it had locked down against his wet leg.

Rising rapidly and gracefully from the creek, Mike jumped completely over the cow. *Whoom!* He was wall-eyed with surprise.

The cow was right amazed, too.

Her hooves churned the water with renewed vigor as he whizzed over her head, setting the perfect example, his wet coveralls flapping like the wings of an angel. She rolled onto her chest, cast her eyes heavenward and gave a great reverential groan. Suddenly, her feet made solid contact with the creek bed. She emerged from the water as if she'd just been baptized and seized by the spirit. I heard the farmer cackle gleefully, and I joined in his rejoicing.

Hallelujah!

That perishing cow might not have found religion, but in Mike, she truly had found an angel—albeit a surprised and perhaps unwitting one.

Chapter 17

A Pair of Medics?

One especially hectic Saturday morning, Maudie the receptionist proved to be as much help to me as she had been to Dr. Oliver a few months earlier, when he told her to give him the water hose and she did.

Most Saturdays, the waiting room is crowded with animals, both sick and well, brought in by people with a long list of things they want to get done that day. The attitude is generally, *Let s get moving! Gotta go! Things to do!*

On this particular Saturday, after ending my shift at the emergency clinic at eight that morning, I raced from Greenville to be at the Easley clinic by 8:30 a.m. The waiting room was already crammed with people and animals when I arrived.

My first patient was a mighty sick basset hound. The owner, a woman with dark circles under her eyes, told me that she had worked all night, then rushed her six-month-old puppy to the clinic as soon as she got home and saw how sick he was. She said he hadn't been able to urinate for a couple of days and was in a lot of pain.

I examined the dog and concluded that a stone had moved out of the bladder and lodged in the urethra. His urinary tract was completely blocked. I knew I had to get that stone out. If I couldn't snag the stone with a loop, I would try to flush it, or push it back into the bladder to be reduced with medication. I hoped one of the less stressful methods would do the trick, so I wouldn't have to do an emergency urethrotomy.

As I examined the dog, I started to tell the weary woman, standing beside her pet, about the options of treatment, so she could give her consent in case I had to do surgery. I had outlined a couple of the procedures when she interrupted.

"I'm feeling kinda hot," she said, fanning the air in front of her face with her hand. I could tell she was about to pass out, but I couldn't let go of the puppy right then to help her.

"Why don't you step outside a minute and sit down in the waiting room, get a little fresh air, and then I'll come talk with you," I suggested, thinking that if she got out of the room, she would be all right.

She nodded. But she had no more than stepped out, pulling the door shut behind her, when I heard a thud in the hall. Too late!

I knew I couldn't get through the door she had just closed without hitting her with the door or stepping on her, so I circled around through the interior of the clinic. As I ran around the receptionist's desk where Pat was working, I saw a man seated on the bench next to the hall. He was holding a cat in his arms. He had a full view of the corridor, but he was staring straight ahead, his eyes deliberately avoiding the woman sprawled face down on the floor within a few feet of him.

109

I couldn't believe it! He was absolutely ignoring the lady who had fainted almost within arm's reach. I stepped around him, giving him a dirty look as I hurried by. I knelt down by the basset's owner and turned her over on her back. Her face was blue, a bad sign. As soon as I saw that, I yelled at Maudie, our receptionist:

"Call the paramedics!"

Maudie leaned over the desk. "The *who?*"

"The paramedics! The paramedics!" I shouted.

She grabbed the phone book. I heard a *schrrick!* I looked up and saw Maudie had torn out a page as she thumbed through the book. She started ripping pages out of the directory. *Schrrick!* There went another page. And another. Maudie was tearing the book apart like a mad woman, searching for a telephone number.

Marcine, our vet tech, had come running when she heard me yell. She applied a cold cloth to the woman's face. We loosened her collar; the blue faded from her lips, yielding slowly to a beautiful warm pink.

Marcine became aware of a strange noise at the desk and glanced over her shoulder at Maudie. Marcine's eyes widened as she saw ripped pages floating like paper airplanes around the reception desk. But neither of us said anything.

We breathed a sigh of relief when the woman on the floor opened her eyes. She was startled when she realized she was lying on the floor, and tried to sit up.

"I'm feeling better," the lady said, embarrassed. "I'm so sorry. I've never fainted before...."

We shushed her apologies and helped her to a nearby chair. While Marcine called the woman's husband to come for her, I walked over to Maudie. She was still frantically looking for the number for the paramedics, much to the delight of everybody in the waiting room. Maudie looked up, bewildered, as I put my hand on her arm and whispered, "You can forget the paramedics."

Calm returned to the lobby, and we got back to work.

We sedated the hound, inserted a catheter and flushed the urethra. The stone washed back into the bladder. The painful, life-threatening situation was eased, and with medication and proper feeding, the lady's beloved puppy should get better.

When the man who had ignored the fainting woman brought his cat into the treatment room, my curiosity, mixed with a little anger, got the best of me.

"Mister," I said, "when that lady started to pass out, why didn't you grab her, so she wouldn't hit her face on the floor?"

He looked me in the eyes and said coldly, "I'm not throwing my cat down for anybody."

Okay, I thought, *so that's how it is. If you think that much of your cat, it's probably worth a little extra for me to treat it....*

Later, Maudie came back to surgery, where we were operating on another patient.

"You know," she told us casually, "that was the first time I had ever seen anybody pass out. I thought I handled myself rather well, didn't you?"

Chapter 18

Pink Slippers

Sometimes good help is hard to find, especially when you're going out on a call alone. You have to depend on owners or caretakers to lend a hand with large animals. A vet who has to depend on volunteers can just about bank on having trouble of one sort or another. It's a rare and wonderful experience when the helper knows what to do and does it well.

I set out alone early one morning to tube worm a dozen horses. Tube worming is not a difficult procedure, but a vet needs a strong, steady helper to hold the twitch in the horse's nostrils. It helps to have someone who can soothe a skittish horse while the tube is slipped into the animal's stomach so the medicine can be inserted.

My destination was a horse farm where the owner had spared no expense to make sure that the houses, barns and pastures at the farm were first-rate. It was quite a spread.

I parked next to the biggest barn, got out and slammed the door of the truck, expecting the noise to attract the attention of the farm's caretaker. No one appeared, so I walked inside and admired the horses I was to treat. Then I waited. And waited some more. I figured I should be able to do the job in a hour—tops. I needed to get to the clinic. As the minutes ticked away, I began to get a little ticked off.

The caretaker who usually helped with the horses lived in a small guest house near the big house. I looked over there, expecting him to come along any minute. At last, I saw the door open, but it was a woman, not the owner's assistant. The woman got in a three-quarter-ton truck and cranked it up. She shoved it in reverse and dug gravel to the end of her drive. The truck fishtailed as she backed into the road to the barn. Then she gunned the big truck's motor, threw it in forward gear and left a wake of gravel all the way to the barn.

I thought to myself, *She may be a woman, but she s going to be good help.*

She pulled up to the fence and opened the truck door. The first thing I saw were her feet swinging out as she hopped to the ground. She had on the biggest pair of pink, fuzzy slippers I'd ever seen. There was no way she could walk in the mud and manure around the barn. Those pink slippers dashed my high hopes.

She tiptoed over to me and asked, "Are you here about the horses?"

"Yes, ma'am. Are you going to hold them for me?"

"Hold 'em?" she squealed at me. "Me hold 'em? I can't hold 'em!"

"Not in those pink slippers, you sure can't" I said.

She explained that her husband must have forgotten the appointment. He had gone to the feed store and had

113

a lot of other errands to do. She expected it would be several hours before he got back.

I thought about the crowded clinic waiting room and my already-full calendar. It would be a couple of weeks before I could get back to worm these horses.

She sensed that I really wanted to get this job done today. She asked, "Just what would I have to do if I helped you?"

I admired her willing spirit, but I now had serious doubts that she would really want to mess with horses, stamping their big feet around her fuzzy size sevens. But she had asked.

"You'd have to hold the twitch in the horse's nose while I put the tube in and get the worm medicine down," I said.

"What's a twitch?" she asked.

Oh, boy. The more she talked, the more difficult this call looked.

"It's a kind of clamp that pinches the nostrils," I told her. "For some reason, the device calms the horse, makes it stand still. It has something to do with the release of chemicals called endorphins, which ease the horse's pain and allows us to work on the animal without anesthesia."

She turned sort of green.

"If it's not too hard, I'll try," she answered. I suspected she was hoping I'd decline such a tentative offer, but I needed to get to the clinic as soon as I could. I grabbed at the straw she offered.

"Fine. That's just great," I told her. "I appreciate it. We'll see how it goes. Okay?"

That lady in the pink slippers proved to be a giant among women.

The first horse made her a little nervous, but by the time we had finished worming the third one, she was a seasoned expert with the twitch. In fact, she began to enjoy the work and even offered to help me on large animal calls.

We put the last of the de-wormed horses in its stall and walked out of the barn, both of us feeling good about a job well done. She climbed up in the big truck. The last thing I saw before she closed the door was her slippers. I eyed those manure-caked pink slippers, and frowned—just for a second. So what? The ruination of those pink slippers had been worth it to both of us.

She revved the motor and drove off, throwing a goodbye wave as the truck's tires tossed gravel.

Although Pink Slippers turned out to be a better helper than either of us thought possible when we started working together, Bubba was an entirely different matter.

Let me tell you about him. Bubba is one big ol' good ol' boy. Humble in intellect, but humongous in physique. Unlike Pink Slippers, who was not sure that she would be able to do a good job, Bubba's personal bulk is exceeded only by his deep well of self-confidence. There's no stopping him when he decides a job needs his expert attention. You might as well try to stop a bear with his arm in a bee gum.

Bubba takes it in mind to help me every now and then. One memorable time he helped, so to speak, at a rabies clinic I was holding at a country church in the hills, near Bubba's homeplace.

The vets in our area take turns holding clinics in rural communities and residential areas to give rabies shots to domestic pets. The clinics provide a valuable public service, but they also are good public relations for the vets' private practices.

One fine spring afternoon, it was my turn, so I loaded my supplies in the truck. As I went out the door with the last batch of syringes, I realized that I had left my jacket at home. So I grabbed a jacket hanging on the coat rack. It had Dr. Mullikin's name machine-embroidered on the pocket.

"He won't mind," I told Marcine, the vet tech who was going to the rabies clinic with me.

When we arrived, the church parking lot was jammed with cars and trucks parked every which way. We got to work as quickly as possible. We were knee-deep in dogs and cats when—over the yipping, growling and meowing of the animals around us—we heard the drone of a big motor.

I looked up and saw the front bucket of a backhoe topping a rise, then its metal shafts, and finally, the cab and rusty chassis. The driver had raised the scoop as high as it would go, and was driving on the road as if he was in a truck. As he got closer, I recognized the driver—my old pal, Bubba. His German Shepherd trotted alongside the backhoe.

The dog was attached to the rusted machine by a thick logging chain. Leaning against the leash as some dogs will do, he advanced erratically, drifting toward the middle of the road until he reached the end of his tether and was hauled back. A couple of cars leaving the parking lot had to swerve to avoid hitting the dog as he veered into oncoming traffic.

This was the first time I'd ever seen anyone dragging a dog to a rabies clinic with a tractor and log chain.

"Now there's one mean dog," I told Marcine. Then I looked at the driver. "Hey, it looks like Bubba's bringing in his guard dog!"

The usual ruckus at a rabies clinic, where cats and dogs meet as strangers with bad attitudes, escalated to uproar as Bubba's backhoe rattled to a halt. His dog contributed his share of noise, hurling deep-throated threats at the crowd.

I nodded hello to Bubba as he oozed off his machine, and watched as he bent down to release the dog's collar from the chain. More spectacle—it was clear to the naked eye that Bubba had dressed for comfort. The brass snaps on the sides of his well-worn bib overalls were undone. His dusty, grease-stained T-shirt—too tight to go over his big belly—had ridden up over the folds of fat and settled under his armpits. A lot of bare Bubba was coming to light.

Bubba grabbed the shepherd's collar and waddled to the back of the line. He greeted the men he knew, most of them retired fellows, who stood in little groups, talking as they waited patiently with their animals. I zapped vaccine into a long line of rumps; then it was Bubba's dog's turn.

The big guy bent over to get a good grip on his dog just as Marcine—who was keeping track of tags and dealing with the paper work—reached across the table to hand me a metal tag. I heard her gasp. I turned to see what was the matter.

Her face glowed like a Rome Beauty. I realized that she had just spotted the wonders of a Bubba in the raw. When he bent over his dog, his loose overalls poked out and gaped wide—I mean really wide—in strategic places. Just as I suspected, Bubba was totally air-conditioned under his overalls.

Marcine's eyelids clicked like a camera shutter. She ducked her head. Papers rustled and metal tags jingled musically at her table. I hid my smile as best I could, and gave Bubba's dog my fastest shot, hoping Bubba was champing at the bit to get back to work.

"Here you go," I said, handing Bubba the metal tag and the slip of paper proving his dog was properly inoculated. "I reckon you have a lot of timber to cut today."

Bubba searched all his pockets until he finally found a wadded bunch of bills and parted with a few of them. "Nawh, Doc," he drawled. "Hit's too hot to work t'day."

The big ol' boy waddled to the backhoe, chained his dog to the machine and came back. His eyes scoped the parking lot; then he informed me, "You're pretty busy, ain't you?" I could almost hear him thinking: *Doc needs me to handle crowd control.*

Bubba took charge. An elderly lady drove slowly into the parking lot and parked close to the tables where we were working. I could hear her cat squalling in a box in the back seat. Bubba lunged for the back door and opened it, saying "Here! Lemme hep ye!"

He leaned over and reached for the cat box. I'll never forget that woman's expression as she looked over her shoulder and saw Bubba. She was the first among many women who drove away that day with a dazed look on their faces. A few earthier types grinned in delight as they thanked Bubba for his kind assistance.

Marcine kept whispering that I ought to do something, but Bubba was too big for me to try to send him home. Besides, he meant well. And anyway, he had allied himself with me.

"Me and Doc are friends," Bubba informed those wide-eyed patrons who were unwillingly captivated by the vision of his gaping overalls.

"We've had us a right busy time here, what with all this crowd," he would say as he yanked a pet from a car or shoved one in.

I ought to be ashamed to admit this, but I was glad that I had left my work jacket at home that morning. Every time Bubba bragged to someone that "me and Doc are friends, don'cha know," I turned so the person got a good look at the name on the chest of my jacket: Dr. Mullikin.

Chapter 19

Taking Care of Dad

The peaceful atmosphere of the Schmidt farm was suddenly marred by a cow that went berserk, bellowing and galloping like a wild thing in the barn. The cow's frenzy upset old Mr. Schmidt, so one of his "boys" called Mike Oliver to come out to "do something about this crazy cow." The events that followed upset Dr. Oliver a good bit, too.

The head of the Schmidt family was in his late eighties. He had three sons. The youngest of the men he called "my boys" was about sixty.

The sons helped their father run the family farm, which supported a small herd of cattle, a few chickens, and some hogs. The vegetable garden fed the four Schmidt families quite well in summer, with enough produce left over for canning and freezing. There was an orchard of apple, pear and peach trees, and the Schmidt wives made fruit pies year around. The fields provided enough hay and grain for the farm animals.

The farmer and his boys were self-sustaining, thanks to hard labor and good stewardship of the land. The sons did the actual work, but they were gentle fellows, who made sure their daddy still felt he was in control of things. So when that demented cow disturbed the old man, one of the boys called Mike.

"She's galloping up and down in between the stalls of the big barn, bellowing, just raising hell," a younger Schmidt said. "We can't do a thing with her. Could you come give her a shot to calm her down?"

"It sounds like grass tetany to me," Mike said. "I'll be out in a little while."

Old Mr. Schmidt came out the back door of the house when he saw Mike park his truck. The three younger Schmidts were already out at the barn. When they saw their father approaching with Mike, one of the sons said, "Now, Dad, you just stay here outside the barn 'til we run that cow into a stall. If we get too many people in there, it'll only make her worse."

Another son found a feed bucket and turned it upside down a couple of feet from the weathered siding on the barn wall.

"You just sit right here for a minute, Dad, and we'll get Sukie penned up; then you can help us," the third son told him.

Mike had been to the Schmidt farm many times before and knew the layout. The cattle barn was long and narrow, with a central hallway and stalls lining the walls. The loft was filled with hay.

For those times when they needed to separate their cows in the barn but outside the stalls, the Schmidts had devised a system that allowed them to divide the barn's middle corridor into several compartments. They had cut three sets of matching slots in both of the two long walls. Then they could slide dividers, made of slender, arrow-straight, skinned pines, through the slots to block off these sections. When the dividers were in position, the ends of the poles were flush with the barn's outside walls.

Old Mr. Schmidt settled comfortably on his bucket, enjoying the warm sunshine. Mike and the Schmidt sons went into the barn, where the cow was bellowing. The thud of her hooves shook the ground as she romped up and down the barn's corridor.

The first pole, then the second pole thunked into place as they were positioned into the slots in the barn walls. The noise level in the barn was raised several levels with the cow bawling and four men shouting as they tried to pen her between the poles.

No one had noticed that the bucket Mr. Schmidt was sitting on was quite close to one of the slots. The old man sat quietly, waiting for everything to settle down in the barn, his gnarled hands resting on his knees, his hat about level with the slot that would hold the divider.

Whoever put the last pole in its slot got distracted before it was properly placed. About eight feet of pine pole stuck out from the barn wall behind old Mr. Schmidt's head, with a couple feet of the short end on the inside.

Inside the barn, Sukie complained with a deafening roar. She gave a mighty lunge, trying to leap over the last pole dangling in the corridor. Her broad chest caught the tip end of the pole, the other end of which was jutting outside. The pole twanged and vibrated wildly; the vibrations quivered along the pine pole to the end that stuck outside. That part jounced and whacked the old man on the head with a solid blow.

Old Mr. Schmidt fell flat, out cold.

He didn't hear the clamor as the four men inside lunged for the cow.

"She caught the end of the pole!"

"Grab it!"

"Grab her!"

"Give her a shot, Doc!"

At last, all was quiet in the barn. Alas, all was quiet outside the barn, too. The sagging doors opened. The sons stepped out to tell their father that it was safe now to come on in and visit the patient.

There lay Daddy Schmidt, sprawled on the ground. All of the boys started yelling: "Doc! Doc! Come quick! Daddy's had a heart attack!"

Mike was inside with the cow, dosing her with magnesium and calcium compounds to ease the convulsive pains of grass tetany, the mineral deficiency that had sent her into a frenzy. When he heard the boys' shouts, he ran outside and saw the old man flat on his face. Mike's stress level shot off the chart.

"Do something!" one of the sons yelled.

Mike thought, *Do what? What do you want me to do? I'm a vet!*

But Mike knelt by the old man, rolled him over, checked his eyes and placed his stethoscope on Mr. Schmidt's chest. The thump of a steady heartbeat brought a smile of relief to Mike's face.

"His heart sounds fine," Mike said. Just then, the old man stirred and shoved his sons' hands aside as they patted his chest and arms, urging him to lie still.

"I'm all right," he insisted. He sat up, rubbing the goose egg swelling on the back of his head. He looked around and saw the pole sticking out from the barn.

"When are you boys gonna grow up?" he sputtered grumpily. "You ought to know how to put them poles in right by now."

They looked at each other sheepishly, relieved that the old man had his senses intact. Finally, he accepted their helping hands. They pulled him up, dusted him off and handed him his hat. They were still too shaken to speak.

Mr. Schmidt settled himself on the bucket and gazed around at the four worried men surrounding him. A twinkle lit his eyes.

"Well, one of these days now, you kids is going to learn to do something right. I may not live to see it, but I've got faith...."

Chapter 20

Mighty Close to Heaven

Our clinic is designed so we can control contact between the animals that are brought in for treatment as much as possible. It helps reduce the spread of infectious diseases. It also keeps down the potential outbreak of hostilities between dogs and cats and other antagonists whose paths may cross in the treatment room area.

I never dreamed that war would erupt between two clients because of a close encounter in a treatment room. It was a moment that still gives me chills.

What happened has everything to do with the personalities of two men who were strangers to each other.

One client was a no-nonsense kind of man who raised top-of-the-line collies. A breeder who had developed a kennel known for its champions, he made ruthless decisions when he inspected his new litters. Any puppy with what he considered even the slightest blemish was destroyed.

Breeding collies was a serious business with him, but it was a sideline. His first calling was to preach. He was known and respected as a pastor who didn't mince words. He was not afraid to step on toes. On this particular morning, though, the collie breeder tromped on more than just the toes of another client—a barrel-shaped man who raised bulldogs and drove a truck with a gun rack over the back seat.

The preacher and the barrel came face to face as I was examining one of the big man's dogs in Treatment Room One.

The bulldog's owner had overflowed into what little space was left over after the dog and I got ourselves situated at the table in that little room. The bulldog breeder was standing between the two doors, watching every move I made, when the door from the hall opened. I looked up, surprised.

The preacher stepped into the room. He didn't say a word, not a "hello" or "excuse me for interrupting." He had his eyes on the open door behind the 55-gallon man. For all the preacher cared, the barrel and I could have been invisible.

I knew my partner Jim was operating on one of the preacher's collies in the back, and I figured the preacher was taking a short-cut to the surgery. I wasn't happy about the intrusion, but I didn't say anything, because I was concentrating on the bulldog.

As the collie breeder pushed his way to the opposite door, he turned sideways and brushed against the belly blocking his path.

The fat man's face turned beet red, and he hollered, "Don't touch my stomach! Don't touch my stomach! I just had a hernia operation, and I don't want it hurt!"

As the collie breeder squeezed by, he glanced down at the belly under discussion and said, "That's a big hurt." Then he walked through the doorway, into the back of the clinic.

I heard the bulldog owner gasp, and chanced to see a blur as he reached into his size 50 coat. I saw his fist wrap around the handle of a holstered pistol.

Quickly, I reached over the table, put my hand on his arm before he got the handgun out of the holster. In as calming and soothing a voice as I could muster, I said, "Let's don't shoot the preacher."

"I don't care if the @#$% is a preacher!" he spluttered. "He ain't gonna talk to me like that! He can't make fun of me!" But he removed his hand from the hidden holster.

To this day, the preacher doesn't know how close he came to Heaven at that moment in Treatment Room One.

In vet school, we didn't have a course on how to deal with gun-toting clients. We thought any potential danger in our professional lives would come from the animals we treated, and we learned to deal with those by experience. But the incident with the preacher and the fat man with the painful belly made me more cautious, though I never expected to encounter another gun-toting client.

So much for expectations.

Several months later, I went out on a large animal call. A cow had been in labor for hours, but no calf was in sight.

When I got to the farm, a man in a high-dollar suit greeted me. A couple of farm workers slouched beside a stall where a cow lay on her side, her huge belly distended, her breath coming in choppy gasps.

I could see just by looking at her that she was close to dying. The man in the suit explained that his helpers had not been able to get the calf turned. I lubricated my hand, tried to reach inside the cow's pelvic cavity, and immediately realized that rough hands had been poking around in there. The canal was swollen and inflamed.

A C-section was the only chance to save her or the calf. I made the incision, and discovered to my dismay that a tiny hoof had perforated the cow's uterus. The inexperienced farm helpers had really botched the job.

Angry and frustrated, I looked up and told the man: "They've just increased the chance of losing this cow and her calf by 75 percent!"

Without a word, he reached back under his jacket. I saw his hand slip a gun out of a hip holster.

Right then I was ready to promise the man his cow would live!

But he put the pistol next to the cow's head and fired. He shot that cow right out from under me.

I couldn't get my equipment together and on the truck fast enough. You can bet I wasn't too hard on him, either, when I sent his bill.

Chapter 21

Home Remedies

"I've tried everthang, I tell you! Jest everthang!"

I could hear Miss Melda talking as I took the last stitch in the abdominal wall of the female Cocker Spaniel on the table. The friendly little blonde Cocker slept peacefully under the spell of the anesthesia. No more puppies for her.

Miss Melda's message reached the far corners of the clinic—not because she was a shouter, but because she had a carrying kind of voice. In the hollers and coves where she lived, such vocal cords came in handy for calling hogs and children to supper.

Miss Melda is one of those folks who consults a doctor only as a last resort. There's no telling how many times I heard the older women in the community where I grew up say that someone "was so sick I almost called the doctor." They will try every home remedy ever known (and some never before imagined) for whatever ails them or their animals. It's an independent streak that runs deep.

I put the sleeping Cocker in a cage to recover and went up front to tell Miss Melda to bring her dog into the treatment room.

She put it up on the table. All I could see was the flat-nosed face of a Pekingese, peering at me from the folds of the faded blue apron in which Miss Melda had wrapped it.

"Doc, I've tried everthang on this dog of mine. It's got the itch real bad, and you gotta do something fer it," she ordered. Miss Melda didn't have a tooth in her head; when she talked, her lips floated in and out of her mouth. Her eyes, like those of her Peke, bulged with anxiety and frustration.

As Miss Melda unwrapped the apron, she told me that the dog had appeared on the doorstep of her home in the mountains one morning, and no one came to claim it.

"Doc, I opened the door, and thar this little dog stood, jest a lookin' up at me. Hit looked jest like an ugly old man," she said. Then she laughed, throwing back her head.

I looked from the dog to Miss Melda. His lower jaw jutted out, a lot like hers, and his lips hung loose. They were a match.

The Peke stood on the table, shivering with fear, look-ing at me with pleading eyes. His coat was a peculiar color—sort of gray-white-brown, with blotches of raw dry skin showing.

"Poor old fella," I said to the dog and patted his back. As my hand touched his brittle fur, a great cloud of dirty white dust rose and floated around us.

"What in the world?" I asked, sneezing as the pow-der went up my nose.

"Hit's Kaopectate," she said. "I told you I've tried everthang!"

I knew she had been desperate if she had poured anti-diarrhea medicine on the afflicted dog. Kaopectate is just about the last thing I'd have tried, too. At least for the mange.

"Miss Melda, your dog has probably got the healthiest mites anywhere," I told her, trying not to laugh. "They sure don't have diarrhea!"

We washed her dog to get rid of the dried Kaopectate, then dipped the Peke in an insecticide to kill the mites. We also sent a supply of medicine along with Miss Melda, so she could continue the dip treatment for her dog at home.

I suggested that she save the Kaopectate for other, more appropriate uses.

As she went out the door, gumming us all goodbye and cradling her dog in the faded blue apron, I thought about home remedies I had encountered.

The garden hose treatment that saved the Eastatoee couple's milk cow was one of the home remedies that worked. Some do. Some don't. Miss Melda's Kaopectate didn't.

But the treatment method one lady tried on her snake-bit dog was the most inventive, most ineffective approach I've heard about so far.

"Doc," she asked when I answered the phone, "what can you give me for my little dog? A snake bit its nose yesterdee, and its face is all swoll up turrable. It's got to have somethin' done about it."

"The best thing to do is bring the dog in," I told her, wondering why she hadn't brought it in yesterday.

"We tried to doctor it ourselves," she said.

"What have you tried so far?" I asked.

"Well," she said, "I stuck its nose in the shop vac."

I nearly dropped the phone. "The shop vac?" I asked, just to be sure I had heard right. I could just see her dog with its nose shoved in the hose of a high-powered vacuum cleaner.

"Yessir," she said. "That's all I could think of."

I tried to follow her line of reasoning. She must have thought the shop vac would suck the poison out.

"Well, did it do any good?" I asked. My eyes watered and my jaws ached with repressed laughter.

"No. Its face swoll up something awful," she repeated. Her home remedy had obviously added insult to injury, but I wasn't about to hurt her feelings.

"You'd better bring the dog in," I told her. "I believe an antibiotic would help it a whole lot more than a vacuum cleaning."

Some folks have the idea that animals and people can share their medicine—that it's interchangeable. Well, it's not.

A topical ointment called DMSO, which is effective in treating animals with sore muscles, began showing up in the medicine cabinets of homes across the country a number of years ago. Arthritis and bursitis sufferers declared it was a wonderful treatment for aching, inflamed joints. Nonetheless, the Federal Drug Administration has not approved it for human use, and scientific studies of DMSO's side effects are not concluded. It has been taken off the pharmaceutical shelves in drug stores, but people still find ways to get it.

Every now and then, someone comes in to the clinic to request a supply of DMSO for a pet or farm animals.

Sometimes their request is based on the truth—and sometimes it's not.

"Doc, I got a horse with a sore shoulder, and I'd like some of that stuff, what you call it? DMSO or something like that." Unconsciously, the client rotates his own sensitive shoulder. Body language starts talking.

"It's the right shoulder, Doc." And he massages his stiff right shoulder, as if sympathizing with his poor old horse's aches and pains.

Yeah. Sure. Sometimes, I'll tell the men who say they want a bottle "for my horse" to exercise caution.

"You have to be careful about putting this on stud horses. It sometimes shrinks their testicles," I'll tell them, trying to keep a straight face. They look pained as they silently calculate how much of the stuff they've already applied to their aching bodies.

What most people don't know is that DMSO is a "carrying agent." It has a penetrating action, and can be used to carry other chemicals

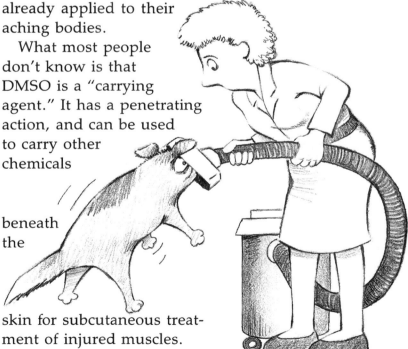

beneath the

skin for subcutaneous treatment of injured muscles.

A friend of one of the drug company representatives who calls on us learned about DMSO's side effects the hard way. It started when the friend, an athlete, began suffering from a severe case of tennis elbow. He got hold of some DMSO to relieve the pain and became an enthusiastic user of the ointment.

He felt so spry that he signed up to run in a five-kilo-meter charity road race. He decided that if DMSO had relieved pain, it might prevent pain, too. Before the race, he applied a liberal splash to his ankles. He rubbed the liniment in thoroughly, and put on red socks to match his running outfit and expensive shoes. Then he set out to establish a personal best record in the five-K race.

It was a hot day. He pounded the pavement on the route through city streets, sweating profusely, his adrenaline pumping. His elbows felt great! His whole body felt great! His ankles and feet felt great—a little hot, but great! He arrived at the finish line with the chosen few—a happy, satisfied runner with a large sense of accomplishment and a little trophy.

Back at his car, he took off his red socks and running shoes, rubbed his ankles and massaged his hot, moist toes. Hmmm. His feet looked peculiar.

In fact, they looked as if he still had on his socks.

To his dismay, he discovered that DMSO—the good carrying agent—had combined with the heat, the sweat and the dye in his socks. His feet and ankles were tattooed a bright, indelible, cherry red.

Chapter 22

If Only We Had a Rope

Anglers, bear hunters, bikers, campers, hikers, horseback riders, and recluses love the Horsepasture. So do I.

The Horsepasture is a natural formation up near the North Carolina line—a spectacular amphitheater ringed almost completely by the cliffs of the Blue Ridge escarpment. Big rivers, including the Horsepasture River, come together there and emerge as Keowee, now dammed to generate electrical power.

The dams back up these cold, swift headwaters into Lake Jocassee, which fills the geological "horsepasture" to a depth, in places, of 400 feet. Beautiful waterfalls spill like lace down the sides of steep cliffs.

Some folks say that during the War Between the States, horses were stashed in the grasslands of the Horsepasture to supply the Southern cavalry. Long before that, the Cherokee lived and hunted there. The place is rich in history, mystery and challenge.

It's not an easy place to reach.

The dirt road into the Horsepasture is a gut-wrencher. For several miles, it follows a snake's trail atop a rocky ridge, with sheer drop-offs that can shift your Adam's apple right up against your back teeth if you get too close to the edge. But the excitement of the Horsepasture is a powerful magnet.

My friend Henry and I decided we were getting stale and needed a challenge. We felt the Horsepasture's tug, so we made plans for a weekend of horseback riding and roughing it in the mountains.

Late one Friday evening, we loaded our two horses in a goose-necked trailer and packed our gear in his dually. We figured to set up camp in the dark, so that we could be up before sunrise for breakfast, with a whole day of exploring and rambling ahead of us. Little did we know that we'd need the power of those extra rear wheels on Henry's truck.

Ideally, if we'd had our druthers, it would have been a moonlit night. Instead, it was overcast, with an occasional glimpse of stars sparkling between floating dark clouds. We drove northward, entered the Eastatoee Valley, then began the hard part of the journey on the dirt and gravel roadbed. The headlights on the truck pierced the darkness; the tires threw dirt and stone as we navigated switchbacks, easing the long trailer around sharp curves.

We talked as we jostled along, laughing as we thought about other trips we'd made together. Henry, who is part-Apache, and I are veterans. We share a mutual disdain for crooked politicians and incompetent military bigwigs. We've had a lot of fun together.

"Remember the time Bucky throwed you out in Arizona, when that narrow-gauge steam engine blew its whistle while you were riding alongside the tracks?"

Henry said, whooping with laughter. "Bucky throwed you so hard, you busted the seams of your jeans!"

"And what about the time you ruined your shirt with tobacco spit?" I reminded him.

"I didn't ruin it!," Henry snapped. "You did!"

I grinned in the dark, remembering the laugh I'd had at Henry's expense. Henry and I had been on our way West. Henry had driven all day and was tired out when we stopped in Texas to refuel. While he went to pay for the gas, I saw his spit cup and a ballpoint pen on the dash. It was a combination too good to pass up. I grabbed the pen and poked a tiny hole in the bottom of the Styrofoam cup, half-full of black juice, and put the cup back on the dash.

I was sitting under the steering wheel when Henry returned. He got in the passenger seat, put a big chew of Red Man in his check, cupped his Styrofoam spittoon comfortably on his chest and propped his knees against the dash. After a few miles, he was doing less chewing and spitting, and more sleeping. Occasionally, he would slip the cup the few inches up to his mouth, spit dark saliva and bits of Red Man into the cup, then ease back into his nap. Every now and then, I glanced his way to check the progress of a small stain oozing down his chest. It grew slowly but surely, a satisfying steady trickle flowing southward toward his belt.

Suddenly, Henry jerked up straight in the seat, and his boots hit the floorboard.

"Dadgummit, Doc! You done it!" His hands swabbed at the wet mess on his chest and belly.

"What? What?" I yelled back, feigning innocence.

137

As we rode together into the Horsepasture, the memory of that earlier trip set us laughing all over again. That trick was only one of many that I pulled on him.

Henry laughed, then grew quiet, concentrating on the road as it got snakier and our surroundings got darker. We were on the part of the road that wilts the knees of anyone who hates heights. On one side of the ridge were cliffs, some falling sharply hundreds of feet to rocky, forested ravines below. On the other, just a deadly little drop-off to the tops of tall poplars and hemlocks. The road is very, very tricky, especially if you're hauling a long horse trailer.

I was telling Henry a funny story as we rounded a sharp turn. The truck slammed to a stop. Henry's chest smashed against the steering wheel and the horn blared. I ate the dashboard. Henry's torso rebounded and the horn was silenced. We were speechless for a second. We knew a wheel had failed to clear the curve, and had, instead, dropped over the embankment.

Henry's soft cussing hissed against the truck cab's windows. I thought I was going to need help to jump-start my heart. Henry cut the motor. The quiet was terrible. We sat still, waiting for disaster. But the truck stayed steady.

We eased out the door with our flashlights and hurried back to the trailer. Things looked bad. The trailer's frame was on the ground, with the left rear wheel suspended over a black hole. The dually and the trailer were balanced precariously on the rim of the ridge.

Inside the trailer, Annie and Bucky nickered and fidgeted. I pointed the beam of light at the edge of the road, surveying the problem. The side door of the trailer opened onto the road bed, but the back door was hanging over the great unknown.

"Hooo, boy! Henry!" I shouted. "We're in trouble."

"Yeah! Tell me about it!" Henry replied. Moving the upper side door of the trailer open an inch at a time, Henry grabbed the halter on Bucky, my quarter horse, soothed him with soft words and led him onto the road. Henry's half-thoroughbred, Annie, antsy even under the best conditions, was in the rear compartment. The trailer and the truck bounced every time she moved. Rocks slithered into the void below. It was unnerving.

"I've got no choice," I told Henry. "I'm going to have to let her out the back and hope for the best. Otherwise, everything's going over the side."

Annie had a slim chance of making it to the road-bed—if she would just turn to her right and step onto the wedge of road rammed beneath the bumper and the right rear tires.

I slid the metal door open with a hellish, hopeless feeling. I turned Annie around and pointed her toward solid ground, away from the dark gaping hole below the wheel. Annie paused a second, disoriented and terrified, not realizing she was on a smidgen of solid ground. She reared and wheeled around. I couldn't hold her. Before I could grab her halter again, she panicked and disappeared into the darkness below. I could hear her falling and scrambling. More rocks tore away from the embankment and clattered down the cliff. Bushes rustled and crackled in her wake.

I acted instinctively. I went after Annie. I scrambled for handholds with one hand, keeping a tight grip on my flashlight as I slid into the darkness behind her, scared to death that at the bottom I would find Annie injured or dying. I was well into my downward, barely-controlled spill before it dawned on me that I might have survived Vietnam, only to die in the Horsepasture.

My descent stopped with an abrupt jolt when my feet struck a ledge. Within arm's reach, I could hear Annie's nervous nicker, and I felt her hot breath against my shoulder. Shining the light around, I breathed a sigh of relief to see her standing between two huge rocks that had saved her from a long free fall to her death. The ledge was just wide enough for the two of us.

I croaked toward the top of the cliff, "Henry! You won't believe this, but Annie's okay! She's opened up a knee, but she's okay!"

She and I were both trembling. I wondered how I was going to get her out of this predicament. I pulled her around so she faced uphill. Annie didn't hesitate a second. She gave two great leaps upward and scrambled to the top of the embankment. She stopped in the road near the truck instead of running away, as I had feared she would do. Henry rubbed and patted her until she settled down; then he tied her next to Bucky. The two horses huddled close, their dark coats disappearing into the black night that enveloped us.

I clawed my own way to the road; then Henry and I gathered rocks to build a bridge under the rear tire. We stacked and braced the rocks against the bank. It was back-breaking work. We were making headway when a faint sound disturbed the deep silence. We stopped and stood listening. A vehicle was approaching. We saw its lights as it followed the twisting road out of the Horsepasture. Then we heard loud voices and laughter. Drunken laughter. What we had was a load of drunks heading our way.

Our dually completely blocked the narrow road. It was dead dark there on the ridge, with only the truck's headlights and our two flashlights shining like little candles under a black canopy.

I ran up the road a piece, waving my flashlight to warn the driver. The truck was pretty close before the driver saw me and slammed on the brakes so hard that the truck fish-tailed.

A man leaned out the open window. "Whazza matter, mister?"

So much for designated drivers, I thought. He was as bombed as the trio of drunks wadded in the cab with him. The bed of the half-ton pickup was a tangle of bodies. They were all hooting and fussing.

"We've had trouble with our truck," I told the driver. "You can't get by."

"Thazza shame, buddy," the driver slobbered, his breath wheezing fumes into my face. I quickly stepped back from the truck.

"If you'll give us a little time," I told him, "we'll get the truck and trailer back on the road, and you can go on by. We've got a couple of nervous horses out here. It'd be best if you all waited in the truck," I suggested.

Instead, they all stumbled out, volunteering to help.

"That's okay," I said, declining their offers. "We'll manage just fine. Y'all set and rest a bit."

The rest of the coots staggered around, then crawled back into the truck, but the driver was determined to be our hero. He followed as I turned back to help Henry.

"If only we had a rope," he said with thick-tongued sincerity. "We could hook you up to my truck and I'd pull you out in jest a li'l minute." He saw himself and his little truck as valiant rescuers.

"Mister, I could pull you out if only we had a rope," the drunk repeated. He looked around at our camping gear in the back of the truck and said, "You sure you ain't got a rope?"

Henry stopped his rock-laying for a minute. Firmly, but politely, he said, "Mister, your truck's not big enough to pull these vehicles out. We'd all be in trouble. We sure wouldn't want anything bad to happen."

Henry and I put on our best manners to deal with our would-be savior. You don't mess around when you're outnumbered by a bunch of drunks in the Horsepasture.

But the drunk driver had made up his mind to be a hero. He crawled on hands and knees along the bank, where we were trying to build the bridge of rocks. He got in our way and made a real nuisance of himself. We had enough danger without worrying about what he might do.

Dodging the drunk, Henry and I got back to work. We packed rocks under the tire, using the jack to hoist the frame a little at a time to give room for the next layer of rocks. All the while, I tried to keep an eye on the drunk. If he went off the cliff, we'd have to haul him from the bottom of the gorge.

He finally crawled onto the road behind the trailer, crooning his little one-verse ditty, "If I Only Had A Rope." It would never make the Top-Ten charts. Suddenly, one of the horses snorted, and we heard a thud in the middle of the road. The drunk let loose an awful groan.

"What in hell was that?" he shouted. I turned the flashlight on him. He was sprawled in the dirt near the horses. Crawling on hands and knees in the dark, he had bumped his head against the belly of a still-jittery horse and got a swift kick.

"Look, mister," I hollered at him, fed up with his antics, "we've got two nervous horses here. If you spook them, they'll run off and we'll never find them."

He blinked at me, turned his head, saw the horses and breathed a deep sigh. "Eh law! Horses! I thought it was a bear!"

Exasperated, I looked around for something, anything to get the drunk out of our hair. Here we were, out in the middle of nowhere, in the dark, with a truck and trailer barely balanced on the bank, and a drunk messing with our nerves.

To my surprise, as I turned around, I spotted a faint glow on the other side of the lake. We weren't totally without help after all! I saw the light of a campfire where some fishermen or campers had settled in for an all-nighter beside Lake Jocassee. A brilliant idea came to me. *He wants a rope. Let him go nd a rope!*

"Mister, look over yonder," I said, pointing the flashlight in the direction of the campfire. "There's some people fishing. You know, I bet they've got a rope. You could help us a lot if you'd go over and ask them if they've got a rope."

The drunk's eyes finally focused on the distant flicker, and his dream of being a hero returned.

"Thazza great idear," he said. He hauled himself up and headed toward his drinking buddies, shouting, "Come on, boys, we're gonna git a rope!"

We heard the truck door slam and a chorus of happy voices as the driver backed the truck to a wide place and turned around. Then the truck zoomed off. In the distance, we could hear the drunks yelling, "Hey, you over there! You gotta rope?"

Henry and I were laughing like crazy men when we packed the last rocks under that wheel. Time to test our engineering skills. Henry got under the steering wheel and inched the truck forward as I stood in the road, giving Henry hand signals. My palms were clammy as the heavy trailer's tire crunched against the make-shift bridge. It held. The trailer was back on track.

We reloaded the horses. Annie's belly and legs were gashed; she needed sutures. We found a turn-around place and left the Horsepasture. Our camping trip ended before it started.

When we got back to the clinic, I sewed up Annie's lacerations and gave her a shot of antibiotics. Henry took her and went home. I left Bucky in the stall at the clinic and I, too, went home. I crawled into bed, exhausted. The disappointment over our lost Horsepasture weekend was tempered a good bit by the truth of how lost it really could have been.

But on the brink of sleep, one question bobbed across my mind: *Reckon those drunks ever found a rope?*

Chapter 23

Gonna Choke 'er Down

Rain splashed in huge drops against the windshield of my old GMC pickup. The wipers swept in great arcs, chasing waterfalls that reduced my vision to a few feet beyond the bumper of the truck. Barely able to see the shoulders of the two-lane highway, I strained to catch a glimpse of familiar landmarks to get my bearings.

Six Mile Mountain looms over the farm of Jess and Mary Floyd, where I was headed. That mountain could have been right in front of me, or 20 miles away. We're talking serious weather, out in the hills.

My wife Betsy had called me earlier on the truck's phone to tell me about an emergency at the Floyds as I was on my way to another farm call. Jess runs a few head of Simmental cattle and dotes on his animals. He takes their well-being seriously.

"Mary Floyd said one of their cows had gone into labor in the pasture and the calf won't drop properly," Betsy told me. "I asked her if Jess had the cow penned up, but Mary said she's running all over the pasture. It's the cow's first calf, by the way."

"I'll get to the Floyds as soon as I can," I told Betsy, "but call them back and tell them it may be close to dark by the time I get there. This storm is not letting up. I just hope Jess corrals her soon, or gets her tied up someplace."

I drove as fast as I dared in the downpour to take care of my first call, to treat a colicky mare. The mare was a gentle old strawberry roan that had raised many colts and all of her owner's children. The youngest teenager had gone to the barn to check on the horse, discovered she was in pain, and called the clinic immediately.

That frightened kid met me in the driveway, drenched to the skin. She ran to open the truck door.

"Here, Doctor Orr, let me carry something," she said, urging me toward the barn. "Roany's real sick."

I examined the horse and determined that she indeed had a mild case of colic. I gave Roany a mild tranquilizer to ease her pain and a generous dose of mineral oil, then told the worried young girl to lead the mare around in the barn for a while. The walk-about would do them both good. It would help the horse, and give Roany's young rider something to do.

"Call me at the house if that doesn't do the trick," I said. "My wife will know where to find me."

Then I headed for the Floyds' farm. As the truck splashed through the gully-washer, I thought about the situations that could be waiting for me.

Betsy had said that Mary Floyd told her Jess had been able to rope the cow, but he couldn't get her close to a post to tie her. I hoped that while I had been working on Roany, Jess had been able to get the heifer tied up. A delayed, complicated delivery was serious. If the half-born calf wasn't taken out soon, Jess's Simmental could die, or be paralyzed by the sustained pressure on the obturator nerve in her pelvic canal.

Either way, Jess faced losing one of his cows. Most likely, the calf was already dead.

The rain slacked off briefly, and a low-lying fog lifted enough for me to see the fence posts lining Jess's hilly pasture. The truck fishtailed up the muddy drive. Leaving the motor running, I hopped out and looked in the barn. No sign of either Jess or the cow. My spirits sank, because I knew Jess was not a man to give up easily. The chase, which had to have begun more than an hour earlier, must still be going on out in the pasture, out in the rain.

I got back in the truck and drove through the gate into the pasture. If I got stuck, Jess could pull me out with his tractor. I stopped on one of the ridges and rolled down the window.

"Jess!" I hollered. "Hey, Jess! Where are you?"

Faintly, I heard him respond, "Yo, Doc!"

I heard his tractor crank up, then the chug-chug of the engine, so I climbed back in and drove deeper into the pasture to meet him. Behind him, as he rolled into view, I could see his herd huddled together on the next hill, barely visible in the gray mist.

"I got a rope around her neck, but it was raining so hard and the rope was so slick, I couldn't hold her," Jess said as he slogged up to my truck. The rain had started again.

"She went back to the herd," he said, as we walked toward the clump of cattle, "and she's dragging 30 feet of rope along with her. I got the tractor out to try to head her off, but that didn't work. The calf's still clamped tight in the birth canal. It's already dead."

147

Jess's yellow plastic raincoat swished as he walked beside me, his pace steady, but not as springy as usual. He'd already put in a long gallop over this pasture. As we got close to the herd, I began circling, lariat in hand. My idea was to slip up on the cow and drop a loop on her so Jess could grab the trailing rope. Once we got her double-tied to a tree or post, I could get on with the delivery.

I don't know how she spotted me in the gray curtain of rain, but she did. She had her own idea: run. I ran, too. Over rocks, through the woods, through briars, old fences, swamps and a swollen stream. Jess was trotting along with us, his face a study in grim determination.

We got her cornered once, just long enough for me to toss my lariat, but the noose slid away. She burst into the middle of the herd again for safety.

The rain was coming down full force again. I stood still for a minute, getting my breath. The rain felt cool and refreshing on my face and back. Jess got his second or third wind. We circled the milling cows.

The mama broke out of the herd. I faked her off, aiming her in Jess's direction. He lunged and caught the rope as she galloped by. For a second, I lost sight of them as they dipped behind the lip of a terrace. Then they came thundering toward me. My heart sank.

Jess had been yanked off his feet and was being dragged face down along the ground behind the cow. In the growing darkness, I followed Jess's wild ride by the glow of his yellow slicker. He slithered right, then left, behind the cow's flying hooves. Jess' body bounced and bobbled. He looked like a water-skier showing his best stuff in a competition at Lake Hartwell. Cow patties and spouts of water splashed in their wake.

I raced toward them, desperate to grab the rope, the Simmental's neck or Jess—anything to stop them. But I could never get close enough. The cow ratcheted to a higher gear when she heard me at her heels.

"Jess! Let go! Let go!" I shouted.

"I'm gonna choke her down," he yelled back.

Jess's body suddenly flipped skyward as the cow dragged him over a huge rock. I flinched as I heard a grunt explode from his lungs as his chest took the brunt of the blow. The rope slid from Jess's hands, and he sprawled, face down, in the soggy pasture.

The Simmental, her eyes protruding with sheer terror and exhaustion, lumbered up the rise to the top of the ridge. The loading chute next to the barn was directly in front of her. The cow unknowingly did the best thing she could have done: She ran into the narrow chute and was penned. She stood still, chest heaving, exhausted.

I raced to help Jess, who lay still for a minute, trying to get his breath. I was relieved when he reached toward my hand and let me pull him to his feet. I saw he was getting his wind back, so I ran to the truck for my bag and the calf chains. We roped the Simmental more securely and maneuvered her out of the narrow chute into the corral, where I would have room to finish delivering the calf.

The exhausted cow lay down in the mud of the corral. I drew lidocaine into the syringe for an epidural anesthesia to stop the contractions. The cow needed to be relaxed so I could attach the fetal extractors and reposition the calf for delivery. Suddenly, she jerked. With a mighty lunge, as if trying to get to her feet, she hurled her big head backward. Jess was leaning over her head, and her hard-boned skull struck his sternum and ribs.

He gasped in pain as he was hoisted off his feet by the force of the blow. His back slammed against the fence planks. He folded inward, and sank as if he were sitting down, into the mud. All expression left his rain-dampened face.

She's killed him! That's exactly what I thought.

I feared the worst as I hurried toward him. Then Jess straightened up, drawing deep breaths and, in the last light of day, I could see his eyes focusing on his Simmental.

"You okay, Jess?" I asked.

"Yeah, I'm all right. Let's get it done," he said wearily.

I repositioned the dead calf and drew it from the tight confines of the Simmental's pelvic bones. It was a beautiful bull, grown too large for the cow to deliver on her own. She had had a rough, fruitless delivery, and I felt bad for her. I administered a shot of antibiotics and inserted a uterine bolus. The large pill would dissolve slowly and help her damaged womb to heal.

All the while, I kept glancing at Jess. He was totally wiped out, and I was scared about him. He didn't argue at all when I suggested that he go on to the house, change into dry clothes and rest before he buried the calf. I assured him that I'd stay with the cow until she got up and went into her stall on her own steam.

Two days later, Jess came to the clinic to pay his bill. I heard the receptionist greet him, and I went out to the lobby to see him, relieved that he was up and moving.

"Man," I said, "you sure gave that cow quite a chase out there in the rain. How're you doing?"

Jess walked over to the door where I stood. He moved stiffly. "I'm okay," he whispered. "A little sore. But I lost my voice. Can't talk. Cow's fine."

My spirits soared. He'd lost nothing more than his voice. Well, certainly a little skin, and easy mobility for a few days. But Jess is one of a tough, rare old breed; he'll do right by his stock—or his family, or his land— or he'll die trying.

It just seemed like belly-skiing behind a heifer through a sea of cow-pies would be a sorry way to go.

Chapter 24

Pig in a Pokey

As a kid, I loved roping calves in our pasture. It was great fun. But in veterinary school, my fellow students and I learned that mastering a lariat was more than a farm kid's trick to impress an audience. It was a skill that would come in handy for those of us who intended to treat large animals.

A long, strong rope is a vital piece of a vet's equipment, especially on small farms where farmers don't bother to build a chute or corral. But truth to tell, few things impress an animal owner more than a vet's well-thrown ringer on the first try.

My partner, Jim Mullikin, has developed a right good hand with the rope over his years in practice. He's proved it time and again to many a large animal owner, but during the wee hours of a dark night, he had a chance to prove his skill to a new audience—not on a farm, but in a mill village in downtown Easley.

The tale of his night's adventure had to be pulled from Jim's mouth like impacted wisdom teeth.

Jim came into work one morning, looking bleary-eyed and rough around the edges. It was his week to be on call, and it was clear that the previous night's duty had been one of those bad times we all dread.

"How'd it go, Jim?" I asked, as he came into the crowded office we share. I always enjoy hearing about my partners' nights of misery.

He grunted—a wordless expression of disgust.

"Bad night, huh?" I said, trying to draw him out. Jim flopped down in his chair. He leaned back, the springs squeaking. He rubbed his eyes and started talking.

"Last night, it was just one call after another. I'd just gone back to sleep about 3 o'clock, 3:30, somewhere along there, and the phone rings again. It's an Easley policeman this time. He says he wants me to come out and help them capture a big boar on a rampage in one of the mill villages.

"Seems the pig tried to attack a man out in his yard. The fellow was about to get in his truck to go to work on an early shift when the boar got after him.

"It's pretty dark, just his porch light and the street light shining at the corner and a nice sky full of stars. As the man tells it to the cops, he's relieving himself in the privacy of his yard, enjoying a quiet moment and looking up at the stars, when he hears this 'woof-woof' sound, a huffing sort of cough, over in some bushes.

"He'd heard the neighborhood dogs barking all night and says he was a little uneasy. So he turns around and sees this big old boar coming straight at him. He could see the bristles raised on its spine, and he swears he could see its beady eyes and tusks shining."

Jim paused and picked up some unopened letters on the desk.

"Yeah," I said, encouraging him, "Okay. So what happened?"

Jim put down the letters and picked up his tale again.

"Well, the man's scared to death. So he dives into the back of his pickup, and that boar tries to gobble up the tires. The guy stands there, trapped, with the boar wheeling around the truck, woof-woofing all the time. Finally, when the pig runs around to the side of the truck away from the house, the man makes his break. The pig charges around the truck about that time, in hot pursuit.

"The guy hot-foots it to the porch, grabs the screen, throws it open. He was one lucky guy! He hadn't locked the door yet. The boar's on his heels all the way, across the yard, up the steps. The pig's plenty mad—dogs must have chased him all over the neighborhood for hours. Who knows where the pig came from in the first place, but he'd been set upon by a pack of dogs. So the boar's out to get revenge on somebody.

"The guy just barely gets in the door. He slams it shut on the snout of that pig. The boar dang near gets in the house! The guy kicks its snout and the boar backs off, madder than ever. "

By this time, Jim's telling his story as if he sees a moving picture in front of his eyes; the film is rolling fast.

"The guy calls the police, tells them a 400-pound pig tried to take off his legs. The officers arrive in their squad car, shining their spotlight every which way. Then they get out and are walking around with their flashlights, and one of them gets a pair of eyes in the beam. Here comes that mad boar, just a-flying around the house in a flaming rage," Jim said.

154

"The officers hop back in the squad car fast and put in a call to—guess who? Lucky me! They tell me there's a boar loose and they need a vet. I get over there; blue lights are blinking up and down the street. Lights are popping on in houses and on the porches. The excitement's got everybody waked up.

"I get my lariat out and walk over to the the police car and talk a minute with them. One of them says the last time he saw the pig, it was headed toward the back of the house next door. I suggest they get out and give me some light with their torches, so we head in the general direction of the pig's last known whereabouts.

"That's when I hear 'woof-woof,' and I know the pig's coming for us.

"One of the cops draws his gun out, ready to shoot. The boar turns on a dime, aiming itself toward him. I fling the rope. The noose settles pretty as you please, even if I do say so," Jim said. He's modest. I could barely make out the trace of a satisfied smile.

"There's a telephone pole next to me, so I wrap the rope around it. The boar makes a couple of twirls around the pole and he's hooked tight," Jim said. "I figure I've done my job, so I head for my truck. One of the officers yells, 'Hey, Doc! Doc! Wait a minute! What we goin' to do with this pig?'

"So I told the cops what to do." Jim stopped talking and fiddled with the papers on the desk.

"Told them what?" I asked.

Jim shoved himself out of his chair. He stood up, stretched and headed for the door. As he walked by, he tossed his answer over his shoulder.

"I told them to throw his ass in jail!"

Chapter 25

Little Horses, Big Troubles

It got to the point that I hated to go out to Feldon's. Not that I dreaded seeing him, or his sweet wife Millie, or his beautiful miniature horses. Oh, no! I love visiting with them when I go on a call to their place.

It's just that, for a while, something bad always seemed to happen every time I showed up to take care of his animals. Calls to Feldon's ended in a guilt trip for me, and bad luck for him.

It all started the day Feldon asked me to come out to tube worm his miniature horses.

Miniature horses are beautiful creatures—tiny versions of their larger kin. And Feldon's were top-rate miniatures. Short as Millie was, the head of the tallest little horse reached no higher than her shoulder. Millie dearly loved the miniatures. She and Feldon lavished nearly as much affection and patience on their horses as they did their grandchildren.

Because the horses were so small, it was difficult to tube worm them. I had to be especially careful, because it was necessary to hold their heads still, and at the same time, make sure the tube went into the esophagus, not into the trachea.

I had finished worming four of the dainty little mares and had only two more to go when Feldon left the corral to bring Boston Blackie, the stallion that dominated the harem, in from the pasture. I would worm Blackie last. Out of the corner of my eye, I saw Feldon leading the stallion toward the corner of the fence where I was working. Feldon had wrapped his hand in the halter, rather than put Blackie on a lead rope.

Blackie frisked alongside Feldon. He pranced, stepping high, a handful of energy despite his pint size. Feldon's arm pumped as he tried to get the horse calmed down. The closer they got to me, the more uneasy Blackie became. His hooves drummed against the hard-packed red dirt. His black mane swirled as he tossed his head.

Feldon scolded the little stallion and pulled down on Blackie's halter. The skittish horse twirled around Feldon's lanky six-foot frame. I grinned, watching the two of them dancing. Then I realized Feldon's hand was twisted in the halter; he was trying to get his arm untangled, and, at the same time, get the horse under control.

Suddenly, Blackie decided he'd had enough. The little horse reared, turning in a tight circle next to Feldon. Blackie lost his balance and flipped over completely, taking Feldon down in a spin with him. Red dust rose around them.

When the two of them finally came up off the ground, Blackie was trapped between Feldon's legs. Feldon's legs are long, but at this moment, they were not quite long enough to touch the ground. He was off balance.

Boston Blackie galloped out to pasture, with Feldon's lanky frame stretched out over the little horse's withers.

I had to wait until I quit laughing before I could get on with my work.

A few minutes later, Feldon trudged back. Blackie trailed at his heels like a dog. Grass stains all over Feldon's pants and shirt, and the pinkish-red dust that powdered Blackie's once-shiny hide, made it clear that the two of them had had another wallow in the dirt before Feldon got the upper hand.

As Feldon's big boots raised dust in the corral, the same smart mouth that got me in trouble in the Navy got me in trouble with my friend.

"Look, Feldon, I came out here to do serious business," I told him, putting on a stern face. "My time is too valuable for you to take off pleasure riding."

He didn't say anything, just shoved his subdued stallion toward me and stalked off. Feldon's temper flare was short-lived. He was his sweet old self before I left. Little did either of us know that this mishap was only round one.

The next time a routine trip to Feldon's turned into a guilt trip involved a cow having trouble delivering her calf. Labor had started, but was interrupted for some reason. The calf's feet were halfway out of the birth canal, but the process had stalled. She was all hunched up, her back arched, straining mightily, but nothing was happening.

Distress at delivery is more common among heifers bred for the first time than among seasoned breeders. Considering the size of calves, it's a wonder that more things don't go wrong. When Feldon called, I hoped it wasn't going to be a repeat of Jess Floyd's bad luck with his heifer.

Feldon met me at the pasture to show me where he had last seen the cow. After searching for a few minutes, I spotted her in the open meadow on top of a hill. I eased close to the cow, my lariat at the ready. She moved off, but I lassoed her on the second try. So far, so good. Now all I had to do was find a fence post or tree to tie her to, so we could get her calf out. She didn't take kindly to the rope. She tugged away sharply, and set off at a brisk trot down the rolling terraces.

I trotted along behind the cow, keeping a loose rein rather than trying to jerk her down or haul her up short. I didn't want her to get panicky. The cow and I loped over one grassy swell after another, heading toward a creek. Between us and the creek was a tree in the middle of the pasture—a perfect hitching post.

The cow seemed to have her eye on the same tree. I let her have her head. At the right moment, I intended to swing out, run around the tree and get her tied safely. She and I gained momentum, loping along at a pretty good pace as we neared the home stretch in the bottoms.

Then I heard a thumping sound behind me and turned my head.

There came Feldon in his big Western boots, running in an unsteady gait, a few steps back. Apparently, he thought I couldn't stop the cow and needed help. He waved his arms and yelled, "Hold up! I'll lend a hand!"

I tried to wave him off. I couldn't explain my game plan, but it was too late anyhow. He grabbed the tail end of the rope trailing behind me. I had to give him some slack, so I released a bit of rope. I thought that the weight of the two of us would be enough drag to slow the heifer down, but she kept moving.

Suddenly, I heard a commotion behind me. I felt rope stinging my palm as it zipped through my fists until I clamped down again. Feldon had let go of the rope for some reason. I looked back and saw why: Feldon was tumbling down the terrace behind me. Head over heels he came. His face plowed a rut in the grass, and he ended his tumble a terrace behind me.

I was hard-pressed about what to do. If I let go of the cow to help Feldon, both his cow and calf were at risk. If I didn't help Feldon, I'd feel like a heel.

The decision was made for me. The cow was almost at the tree, and I was only a few feet behind. I ran wide to the left, doubled back toward the cow, ducked under the rope and whipped the lariat around the tree. The cow stopped in her tracks. I hitched her quickly, then ran toward Feldon. He was back on his feet, gamely walking down the hill toward me. One shoulder drooped, and his elbow stuck out. I could tell by just looking that Feldon had a broken arm.

"Feldon, let me get you back to the house so Millie can take you to the doctor," I said. But Feldon is tough.

"No, let's see about the cow first," he said. "Then we'll tend to the arm."

What saved the day for me was the live, healthy calf I delivered a few minutes later. It wobbled close to its mother. Calm at last, she licked its damp hair with her rough, broad tongue as the calf began nursing.

Then Millie and I took Feldon to his friend and physician, who lived just up the road. The doctor felt the arm and nodded.

Feldon had a broken arm, and I felt rotten.

The next time I went out—this time to see about an ailing little mare—I shot a quick glance at the sky to see if a black cloud was anywhere in sight as I got out of the truck. There wasn't. Not at that moment, anyway. I took care of the minor problem with the mare and drove off, breathing a sigh of relief.

I turned onto the main highway and headed for the clinic. Glancing behind me, I could see great dark clouds in the distance, boiling up against the clear sky.

Could that be at Feldon s? I asked myself.

Nahhh....Everything was hunky-dory when I left. It couldn't be Feldon's.

I should have known better than to talk myself into believing the jinx was over. A couple of days later, I learned that Feldon's barn caught fire shortly after I left. Feldon reassured me, telling me that, fortunately, no animals died in the fire, which started from an electrical short circuit at the fuse box.

"Aww, it was just an old barn," he said, consoling me when I told him how sorry I was to hear of his trouble.

The thing that makes me feel so guilty is this: Feldon is always so glad to see me. He welcomes me like a long-lost friend. I think it speaks well of a man who can be so gracious to the fellow who seems to bring bad luck every time he calls on him.

Chapter 26

Art Is Part of Heart

One of my favorite professors taught anatomy. He was a gifted teacher. His mind was an encyclopedia crammed with an awesome knowledge of the interior structure of animals. His exams were sweat-soakers.

One of his innovative techniques of teaching was to pass thick cotton socks, tied at the top, among us. Each sock contained an animal bone. Using only the tips of our fingers, we were required to deduce information from the hidden bone to create an image of the creature it had once been part of, and how it fit into the animal's body. The professor expected us to tell him not only what animal the bone in the sock came from, but also whether it was on the right or left side of the animal.

During one lab, one smart aleck threaded waxed string through the leg of an animal he was dissecting. Feeling he was a clever fellow who was going to stump the professor, he called the professor over and said with faked consternation: "Sir, I can't figure what this nerve is. It's not shown in the text book. What do you think it is?" The rest of us waited as the professor bent over, glanced at the white strand, and turned away.

"String."

In addition to anatomy, he taught us how important a sense of humor as well as the sense of touch is to a veterinarian.

In later years, when I began sculpting animals in bronze, I was doubly grateful to the professor for his bone-in-a-sock exams.

I became a sculptor because I was awe-struck by the bronze pieces created by Frederick Remington and Charles Russell. I saw works by Remington and Russell in a museum when I was traveling out West. Their artistic greatness kindled a creative spark in me; I yearned to capture the grace of birds and animals in some enduring form, and my fingers itched to give sculpting a try. I felt sure I could do it, but I had no idea what was involved in the process. I had never had an art lesson, and didn't know where to start.

Soon after I got back from the trip, I asked an experienced sculptor to recommend books I could read to learn bronze sculpting. With a busy schedule at the clinic, I doubted I would have time to take classes.

When I told her I wanted to do bronze sculptures, she blurted out, "You can't do that! That would be like me operating on an animal without going to school! It takes years of study."

I was dead set on trying my hand at sculpting, and was not about to be discouraged by what she or anyone said. I read everything I could find on the subject. Then I met an artist–teacher, Claude Davis, whose specialty was bronze casting, and he helped me develop the techniques I had to learn.

He and I built a furnace in my shop. Without his help, I might have blown the place up or burned it down. Though I now send my molds to a foundry to be cast, the lessons I learned from Claude and in the "trial-and-error school" have been valuable. I discovered there's always something new to learn and a new way to do things. Every bronze sculpture I complete is a new adventure. A sense of accomplishment and satisfaction wells up inside me whenever I see the finished work, and it's a joy to share my work with someone who likes what I have done. I am delighted when someone buys a piece I have made.

Little did I dream, when I was driving a fuel truck at the military base at a beach near Da Nang in Vietnam that my future would hold a career which satisfies me and gives me a chance to do something meaningful and useful, a wife and son who enrich my life and give it zest, and a hobby that releases the creative juices in me.

I remember driving by the Da Nang depot where aluminum coffins containing the remains of those who had died were piled high, like cordwood. As I passed the depot, I could see front-end loaders wheeling about, adding more boxes of bodies to the stacks, or loading them into cargo planes for the last trip home.

Oh, the tragedy of those boxes. Every one of them had a broken heart in it. It made me think of Mama, knowing how she worried about one of us coming home in a box. More broken hearts were waiting for those lost lives to be brought home for burial. I promised myself that I'd never forget those coffins— that if I lived, there wouldn't be another lost life because of 'Nam; that I would somehow make up for the wasted years I'd let slip by.

I've learned a lot of important lessons since then.

Ms. Jones taught me there's no shame in dropping back to punt if you must. My dad taught me and my brothers that no one owed us a living, and Mama reminded us, especially when we were in trouble, that it was up to us to make something of the lives we'd been given. She must have told me a hundred times that I had to keep trying.

"A constant drop of water will wear away a stone," she'd say, and her smile would light her face.

On the beach in Vietnam, staring at those boxes, I swore I'd never give up.

It might have been a near thing, once or twice, though. Every now and then, something has come up that made me think my life was in one of the professor's old socks. Then I remember Mama's smile and I remember her words. She knew what she was talking about. Many a drop of water has smoothed away some of my rough edges.

Chapter 27

Rerun and Daktari

Little did Dr. Ron Outlaw realize how big a favor he was doing a bull calf by giving him a good home with the adventuresome young son of one of our clients.

The scrawny calf was injured during delivery. The owner didn't have time to bottle feed a weakling, so he told Ron if he wanted to try to save it, the calf was his.

Ron brought the newborn to the clinic, put its leg in a cast, bottle-fed it and mothered it until the calf began to thrive. A couple of months passed, and the calf outgrew the space in the clinic's pen. Ron had to find the little bull a permanent home where it would have room to graze and roam.

An idea hit him: Wouldn't Rerun love a baby bull? Rerun liked nothing better than to take care of animals, especially young ones. Ron called Rerun's parents to offer their nine-year-old boy the calf.

"You want Rerun to raise a bull?" Mitch asked him. "Our Rerun?"

"Sure," Ron said. "He'll do a fine job. It'll be good for Rerun and the calf, too."

Mitch pondered the offer silently for a minute, then asked Ron to hold the phone while he talked it over with Rerun's mother. Ron could hear a woman's raised voice as she asked, "Say what?"

More muffled sounds ricocheted between them; then Mitch got back on the phone.

"She said she guessed it would be all right. We'll give it a try," Mitch said, his voice conveying a lot of doubt. After all, he lives with Rerun. More to the point, Mitch is responsible for Rerun.

The staff at our clinic had never met Rerun, but they'd heard a lot about him from his dad when he came in to get medicine or bring an animal in for treatment. It was clear that life with Rerun was never boring. He was all boy, full of enthusiasm and energy, and absolutely fearless.

We got a lot of entertainment from hearing about Rerun's adventures. We were also relieved that we didn't have to be responsible for such a precocious kid.

Mitch often said that living with Rerun was like living with a firecracker with a long fuse: He knew it would go off sometime; he just didn't know when. It was the anticipation of the explosion that kept him on edge.

Like the time Mitch was filling a prescription at his pharmacy and Rerun called. "Daddy, bring a wrecker when you come home," he said.

"Why? What's happened?" Mitch was too slow. Rerun had hung up.

Had Rerun's mother had car trouble? Oh no! What if she'd had a wreck? Mitch was in a panic when he called home, and grateful when his wife answered a little wearily, but not in terrible distress.

167

"No," she said, "nothing like that. Rerun was trying to do a trick with the golf cart, and it went wrong."

"What do you mean, *wrong?*" Mitch visualized the golf cart they used to ride around the farm wrapped around a tree. He was not prepared for her answer.

"He drove it at top speed up a ramp, trying to jump across the pond. It nose-dived into the water," she said. "He says it didn't have enough power."

Another time, Rerun again called Mitch to order a wrecker, again hanging up before Mitch could ask a single question.

Mitch's fingers trembled as he dialed his home number. His wife answered, and Mitch hollered, "What's wrong? Why did Rerun tell me to get a wrecker? Are you all right?"

His wife sighed and explained, "Rerun just started up your backhoe and drove it into the lake."

Mitch hurried home and ran to the lake. All he could see was about two feet of the backhoe's back boom sticking above the water near the shore. He cornered Rerun and asked the question a parent should never ask a nine-year-old: "Why?"

Rerun had a perfectly logical answer: "I was just checking the carburetor, Dad, like you showed me. That's all."

That's Rerun.

Mitch suspected the bull calf would be a mixed blessing, but he was willing to take the gamble for his boy's sake. Maybe taking care of the calf would channel Rerun's explosive energy.

Mitch and Rerun came to the clinic to pick up Ron's gift. The kid was thrilled. He rubbed his hands all over the calf's face, patted its hide and examined the knobby little horns and hooves with the concentration of a farmer contemplating a major purchase.

"Thanks, Dr. Outlaw," Rerun shouted, hanging out the window of the truck as they drove off with the calf in the cattle hauler. "I'll take good care of this calf. Thanks a lot!"

Rerun named his new treasure "Daktari."

Months went by. Then one day, Mitch stopped by to get some medicine for a sickly goat.

"How's Rerun?" I asked. "And how's the bull?"

Mitch rolled his eyes.

"You won't believe this," he said. Then he added, "No, maybe you will."

It was almost quitting time. The last patient had left. Most of the staff had circled around us when they heard Rerun's name mentioned. We waited, smiling with anticipation.

"What happened was this," Mitch explained. "Rerun and the bull made up this game—a butting contest. Rerun drives out to the pasture in the golf cart, and he and Daktari fight to see which has the most power. Daktari puts his head against the bumper of the cart and pushes, then Rerun stomps on the golf cart pedal and pushes. The one who gets the most distance wins."

Mitch threw up his hands as we laughed. "I didn't know about this game 'til the other day. If I had, I'd have stopped it a long time ago. But we can't keep an eye on Rerun all the time."

We nodded sympathetically. We could tell Mitch needed to talk.

"Rerun got to bragging to his classmates he had a rhino at home. One little kid asked to come see that rhino. He didn't quite believe Rerun, but he wanted to make sure.

"So Rerun invited the little boy to come home with him after school. I didn't know anything about this, you understand. I was unloading some sacks of feed in the barn. I kept hearing this strange sound outside against the wall, a gasping sort of sound, and thought one of the goats might be choking on something. So I hurried outside.

"I saw this little fellow, a stranger, spread-eagled against the barn wall, his chest heaving, sucking air like he was about to draw his last breath. He was plastered against the wall. The boy's eyes were about to pop out of his head.

"Scared me, I'll tell you! I didn't have any idea why he was at the barn, who he was or what was wrong with him. I thought he might be having an asthma attack. I started talking as calmly as I could. He grabbed hold of me and started pointing at the pasture.

"He couldn't even talk. Man, I was worried. Then I saw Rerun driving the golf cart over the rise, flat out flying, and I knew half the answers to my questions already.

"Rerun throws that cart out of gear, jumps off, runs to his friend and shouts, 'Why'd you run? Daktari won't hurt nobody! We do that all the time!'

"The little boy shifted behind me and glared around me at Rerun. It was clear he didn't believe a word Rerun was saying. He kept darting looks at the pasture and wouldn't let go of me.

"I asked Rerun what happened. He said his school friend wanted to see Daktari, so the two of them rode out and the bull wanted to play.

"Rerun said Daktari chased and butted the cart, and it scared Jimmy, and he jumped out of the cart and ran like the wind to the barn.

"Rerun told me he had the pedal to the floor, but he couldn't catch Jimmy. That bull isn't so little any more," Mitch said. "I don't blame the kid for being frightened. We've stopped that game. I hope."

Mitch stuffed the medicine in his pocket. He headed toward the door and paused for a second, then added, "I sure hope Rerun doesn't find where I hid the keys to the cart." He sighed deeply. "But I won't count on it."

We agreed among ourselves as Mitch drove away that Rerun already had the keys, and that he and his "rhino" probably were, at that very moment, having a grand old time testing their strength against each other.

Rerun would win. He always did, one way or another.

Chapter 28

"Don't Let Him Hurt You, Sonny!"

Why anyone would build a barn with a five-foot-high door, I'll never know. But the spry old man just pointed to the pint-sized, weather-warped door, and said, "He's in there."

It was going to be another tight squeeze, but what was I to say? The barn was older than Mr. Hodges and he was ninety-two. It was probably built by a great-great granddaddy; I read someplace that people back then were shorter than we are now. At least this one was, or else he was kind of strange.

Anyway, I was standing there feeling like Gulliver, and Mr. Hodges was feeling anxious about his Polled Angus bull.

"He's blowed up big as a Goodyear blimp," the farmer said. The animal had overindulged in the turnips the old farmer had hauled home from the loading dock of a local supermarket. The produce manager often gave Mr. Hodges a bushel or two of turnips, too withered to be sold. Cattle love chopped turnips, but too many can cause bloating. Mr. Hodges's gluttonous bull was suffering the consequences of a big dinner.

Mr. Hodges stood back as I stooped and ducked my head to clear the low doorway. I stepped into the gray dimness of the ancient barn, my rope in one hand and my vet bag in the other. As I waited for my eyes to get accustomed to the shadows, I put the bag down and lifted my eyes to peer around and find the bull's stall in the small barn.

I sucked air!

I was eyeball to eyeball with the biggest Polled Angus bull I'd seen in years. The whole barn was the bull's stall. He was free to roam where he willed. In the dusty streaks of light spilling through the slightly opened door behind me, I could see that he was willing me to get out of his way. His eyes spoke volumes: *Get outta my space!*

I did. I backed out, banging the back of my skull on the top ledge of the doorway as I retreated. The bloated bull marched forward as I stepped back out into the sunlit corral where the old man waited patiently.

My lariat, thank goodness, was still in my hand. I had not dropped it to the ground when I put the bag down. The bull blinked in the bright light, and I quickly put a loop around his head. The animal was so bloated that he was not interested in a rousing demonstration of his strength. His hide was stretched to its outermost limits.

"You're absolutely right, Mr. Hodges," I said. "He does look like a blimp." I took up the slack on the rope, dragging the bull up to the wooden corral. I thumped the bull, listening to the vibrations, explosions and rumbles inside his four-chambered stomach. Enough gas to power a small engine was trapped inside.

I retrieved my bag, pulled out the speculum and got a good hold of the bull's head, tilting it backward. I started to insert the metal pipe into the bull's mouth, but the moment it touched his tongue, the bull went berserk. He threw his head against my side and pinned me against the planks. He kept leaning and pushing. I couldn't get out! I felt the pressure increase on my rib cage, and the thought flashed through my head: *He'll mash me to death!*

The nearest locust post creaked and then I heard it crack and break off at ground level. The plank behind me gave way a little as the post broke, and my chest moved backwards a few inches from the bull's head. I grabbed a breath. Then the bull butted me again, and the two adjacent posts snapped.

For a couple of minutes, the springy old boards and the bull had themselves a ping-pong match. I was the ball. The boards flexed like a springboard; whenever the bull stopped pushing and stepped back, the fence boards would slap me forward against his head. I just kept bouncing back for more.

Every time the bull bashed me, I could hear Mr. Hodges yell out, "Don't let him hurt you, Sonny!" The old man didn't offer to come to my rescue, so I wasn't sure whether he was shouting encouragement to the bull or me.

Finally, when the bull stepped back for one more go, he delayed his ping-pong serve long enough for me to duck down and crawl, on all fours, out of the blimp's reach.

Battered and bruised, I was a little put out with Mr. Hodges. Old as he was, I didn't expect him to jump in whole hog, but I thought he might at least have been able to whack the bull's rump with a stick or something, to distract the critter 'til I could get away.

When I got my breath again, I got the blimp anchored down, knowing that no help was going to be forthcoming from Mr. Hodges. Somehow, throughout the match, I had kept hold of the metal speculum, for fear that the bull would swallow it. When I crawled off, I took it with me.

On my second go-round with the bull, victory was mine. I got the speculum between the bull's teeth and inserted a smaller flexible pipe down its throat toward the rumen. I felt resistance in the esophagus before the tube reached the first chamber of the stomach.

"He's got a chunk of a turnip caught down here," I said as the pipe stopped advancing. The trapped chunk had closed the passageway, and methane gas had built up in the bull's abdomen.

Mr. Hodges had come up on the other side of the bull just at the moment the tube touched the blockage in the esophagus. The bull's head was turned at an angle away from me—pointed right at Mr. Hodges—and when the tube and the chunk of turnip collided, the chunk of turnip popped into the rumen.

"Watch out, sir," I yelled, trying to warn the farmer to get out of the way, but it was too late. Immediately, a great, hissing rush of methane gas erupted from the tube, right into Mr. Hodges' face. The stream of foul-smelling fumes gushed from the bloated bull's innards like a Texas oil well.

The old man jumped backward, his hand over his nose and mouth. I couldn't let go of the bull. Mr. Hodges staggered away, leaning against the fence and holding on with one hand 'til he got some distance between his nose and the spewing methane. I watched him nervously. I didn't know how strong a constitution he had. But Mr. Hodges was tough. He had not reached his ninth decade by being a wimp.

"Lordy, lordy," Mr. Hodges said finally. He wiped tears from his wrinkled cheeks. "That was a close call!"

I turned away, my shoulders shaking, and tried to hide my face in the bull's neck. But then Mr. Hodges started guffawing, and so did I.

The bull was as meek as a happy baby. I removed the tube and the speculum. I thumped and listened. The sounds I heard were normal again. I loosened the rope, and the deflated bull waddled to the rusted bath tub that was his watering trough. The bull lowered his head and slurped heartily. A satisfied comment floated from the animal's hindquarters.

"I guess it's true that all's well that ends well, Sonny." Mr. Hodges said. I left him leaning against the fence, admiring his bull, and laughing.

Ordinarily, I'm not partial to sweet gum trees. Anyone who's tried to clear them from a pasture knows a gum tree is well nigh impossible to get rid of. Cut one down, and little sprigs will pop up all around the stump, each stem determined to survive and thrive at the foot of the parent tree. A gum tree's grain is so twisted that it's not even worth splitting for firewood.

But as I dodged the horns of a mad Brahma cow one day, I blessed the sweet gum stump I was dancing on. To me, right then, "sweet" was a significant word. Spindly little offshoots surrounded the decaying stump, making a leafy bowl that I had jumped into during a desperate attempt to protect myself from the angry longhorn. The knee-high shoots entangled her horns as she tried to spear me.

The situation is turning mean, I thought, as I leapt high to avoid another jab of sharp spikes. Her horns spread wider than the span of my outstretched arms, and she was determined to pierce my tender body with one or both of the sharp points.

My dilemma had become clear almost immediately after I arrived at this sprawling farm near Pickens. The cattleman had called about a cow with a partial prolapse of the uterus.

The ailing Brahma was in the barn, so I went in to make an initial inspection of the situation. Right away, I was impressed. I saw her dark form silhouetted against the open door at the other end of the central hall. She stood tall, holding her horns high. She looked regal, powerful. With the spread of her horns, she could have posed for any steakhouse billboard.

The Brahma became aware of my presence. She turned her great head and looked over her shoulder. She whirled, lifted a hoof and threw dirty straw behind her. Just in case I hadn't noticed, she shoveled dirt with the other hoof, then moved in my direction.

I quickly stepped out of the barn into the corral. The cattleman, who had stayed outside the fence, was a gentleman farmer. He wore a high-dollar suit, and propped a well-polished boot on a rung of the metal gate. I could see white cuffs sparkling as he rested his elbows on the gate. He owned the herd, but he wasn't the type to get down in the dirt with them. He paid somebody to do that sort of thing. But his hired hand wasn't around, and I knew I couldn't expect the cattle-man to offer assistance if I needed help.

"Where's your headgate?" I hollered. There was no sign of a wooden contraption to brace her head and hold her steady. Something was going to have to hold her still; her leathery womb had popped out, and was flapping around her rump. I was going to have to clean it and push it back into place, and I needed her full cooperation.

"Headgate?" He acted as if he was surprised. "You've got your rope, don't you? It's you and your rope."

Oh, boy, I thought. *He's one of those who takes pride in not having a chute or a headgate for the convenience of vets he calls in to treat his cattle.*

Realizing that he wasn't about to get his hands dirty, and that I was out here all by my lonesome with his Brahma, I lost a lot of my enthusiasm. I am fully aware of the sometimes dangerous aspects of the veterinary business, but I am not foolhardy to the point of being stupid. At least, not as a general rule.

Behind me, I heard the Brahma canter into the corral, and I knew she was looking for me—or anybody—on whom she could vent her ill temper. She was hurting, and she needed somebody to blame. The corral was surrounded by a six-foot-high chain link fence. There was no protecting pipe across the top. I was looking at a lethal row of spikes. I didn't want to have to go over that fence with a mad Brahma charging.

As I was checking my chances and studying the risks, I noticed that the Brahma was half-hidden by a patch of sweet gum suckers, growing out of the base of an old tree stump. The bushes were the only vegetation—in fact, the only objects—in the red clay corral besides the cow and me.

I eased to one side of the corral; she ran around the opposite side of the bushes and headed flat out for the barn. I decided I would make one toss of the rope—just one—to save face. If that failed, I was going to bow out and tell him he'd have to get a headgate in place before I tackled the prolapsed uterus. I wasn't about to admit I was afraid of her. I made a half-hearted throw of the lariat, aiming high.

Oh, rats! The loop blossomed open and settled around her wrist-thick horns as gently as a caress. I'd have been admired at any rodeo with such a toss, but at this particular moment, I wasn't aiming to win. I braced myself for the shock as she hit the end of the rope. The rope jerked tight against my fist, and she turned on a dime.

Like a rifleman looking through a scope, she sighted down the taut rope. She glared back at me along that stretch of nylon as if I was the bull's eye on her target.

She charged. I ran. I was still holding my end of the rope. After a couple of laps around the corral, she was gaining on me. I looked around wildly as I ran. The gate of the fence seemed a couple of miles away. I'd be gored before I reached it. The metal spikes along the top of the fence would rip me to shreds.

I was desperate. I spotted the sweet gum stump and leaped. I landed in the bushy bowl barely ahead of the Brahma's horns. I wound my end of the rope around the sturdiest saplings, looping and weaving the slack as I danced and dodged her horns. Finally, I had woven a clever trap: the Brahma's eyes stared into the stump, and my shins and body were safe. Momentarily.

179

By now, I was really mad, and determined that I'd show that cow and her owner what a real veterinarian was. I retrieved my bag, loaded a syringe, and gave her a shot of anesthesia. With no help whatsoever from the cattleman, I tugged and shoved at the Brahma's big body until I got her pointed downhill on the slightly sloping corral. The force of gravity was all the help I was going to get while I shoved her uterus back inside her body.

It was a piece of work—like trying to stuff an inflated life raft back into a small plastic bag. When I finished, I retrieved my lariat, picked up my bag and stalked out of the corral.

"I've got another call to make. You can stay and watch her 'til she wakes

180

up," I snarled at the cattleman as he opened the gate. "She's all yours."

I was halfway back to the clinic before I realized that I'd snatched a long twig of sweet gum as I left the corral, and I was chewing on the stick. Just as I used to do when I was little and thought sweet gum was a chewing gum tree.

How sweet it was again. How sweet to be alive and chewing.

Chapter 29

The Perils of Snake Breath

Bubba's wave worried me.

Usually when we meet, his beefy arm goes up like a flag pole, and his hand fans the breeze. My old buddy Bubba is the one whose air-conditioned overalls caused such a sensation among the ladies at a rabies clinic one hot summer day. He is always an enthusiastic greeter.

But not this morning. I was out for my regular morning jog along the edge of my neighbor's pasture. Despite the distance, I could tell that something serious ailed Bubba. It was much too early in the morning for him to be tired. Bubba's wimpy wave signaled trouble.

Bubba turned my neighbor's tractor into the field, driving slowly and carefully. That was another thing that worried me, because Bubba generally guns a tractor around as if he's rounding a turn at Darlington.

My neighbor, like a lot of other farmers in our part of the country, hires Bubba from time to time. For one thing, Bubba comes up with all sorts of rare wisdoms.

He told this neighbor the other day that he sure was glad the corn crop was in—because, he said, "we gon' have hail today."

"What makes you think that?" the neighbor asked, fooled by the sunny sky.

"I heared the weatherman say it this mornin'," Bubba warned. "Says, 'Expect ice-o-lated showers.'"

Bubba's main thing is heavy machinery; he makes his living driving logging trucks and big farm equipment. My neighbor regularly hires Bubba to bush-hog his pastures, and harvest grain and hay. That 500-acre farm adjoins the smaller place where Betsy and I and our little boy Ethan live.

I was worried about Bubba. So I cut across the field on a trajectory that would connect me with the tractor as Bubba cut his first swath of fescue. He saw me heading his way and cut the motor. He sat there on the John Deere, his big rear end overflowing the metal seat, just waiting.

"Bubba," I called out as I got close to the tractor, "what's wrong? You okay?"

Bubba could have been a model for the artist who illustrated *The Jungle Book*. Like Baloo, the bear, he's pear-shaped. His hefty body quit fighting a battle with gravity when gravity started winning. Bubba's bulk starts at his neck and flows downward in folds. This morning, he was pale. His fluffy cheeks drooped more than usual. His deep-set eyes were downcast and sorrowful.

" 'Lo, Doc," he said in a weak voice. "How ya doin'?"

"I'm fine, but you're not looking so hot," I told him. "What's the trouble?"

Bubba eased himself off the tractor in a slow ooze and leaned against the back tire.

"Yer right, Doc," he wheezed. "I ain't doing so hot. I dang near died yestidy."

"You what?"

"I might nigh died, that's what," he said. There was a note of profound sadness in his voice, but, because I know Bubba, I also detected the faintest hint of pride.

"What are you doing out here cutting hay, then?" I asked. "Oughtn't you to be in bed? What happened?"

"Well," he said, scratching himself freely, as was his habit. He settled himself more comfortably against the tractor. I realized I was in for a full account of his close call, whatever it was.

"What happened was this, Doc. You know the Colbys? The folks that built that fancy place over yonder, not too fer from here?"

I nodded.

"Well, I was over thar, clearin' up around the place, cuttin' grass, thrashin' the bushes off the banks, that sort of thang," Bubba said. "I was using the swang blade on this high bank aside the pond, don'cha know, when hit happened."

He paused. A soulful, remembering look came into his eyes. I waited and waited. Finally, he went on.

"Yessir, that's when hit happened. I took a big whack high up on that bank, and right there in my face was the biggest copperhead snake I ever seen. Lord, hit was huge, Doc! Just huge!"

"A copperhead! What happened?" I tried to prod the story along.

"What happened, Doc, that copperhead, hit breathed on me! Yessir. Blew hits ol' breath right in my face!"

Bubba paused again, the enormity of his danger apparent to him, if not to me.

"The copperhead breathed on you?" I said, my lack of understanding telling in my voice.

"You know hits breath is pizen, don't you?" he said.

I was almost ashamed to admit that I was unaware of this universal truth. "No, I didn't," I said.

"Yessir! Hit sure is. And that thing breathed on me! I near died right there! I went weak in my knees. I knowed I didn't have long afore that pizen finished me. I 'membered they was a phone in the little building aside their swimming pool, so I crawled over thar, but the damn door was locked," he said.

Bubba's eyes grew wide as he went on. "So what I did was I crawled on my hands and knees to my truck, don'cha know, and I kindly coasted all the way in to Liberty to the doctor's office."

"What did the doctor do, Bubba?"

I could hardly wait for the answer.

"Why, Doc, she treated me from snake breath, that's what! Saved my life, she did."

Good old tough Bubba was now perhaps the world's only survivor of snake breath. He stared dramatically out over the fields, his vision taking him far beyond the mountains. After a pause, to allow me time to think about his near-death experience, he cut his eyes around to see if I was impressed.

It's bad to disappoint a friend. I stared back at him with open-mouthed amazement.

"You're lucky to be here, Bubba. Real lucky," I said.

Sure enough, there was a glint of pride in his eyes. He straightened, climbed bravely on the tractor and his posterior spilled over the seat. "Well, Doc," he said, "I better get to work. Doctor said that's what I needed to do to get this thang off my mind."

With a wilted flip of his hand in farewell, Bubba rode off into the rising sun. And I ran home to warn Betsy about snake breath.

Chapter 30

The Rehabilitation of Little Bucky

The couple who brought in the fly-blown fawn were both near tears.

"We found this baby deer when we were hiking on Sassafras Mountain this afternoon," the young woman said. The tiny creature, about a week old, was a bag of bones, and near death.

"We watched for two or three hours, waiting for the mother to return, but she never did," the young man explained.

His girlfriend gently touched the fawn she had wrapped in her sweater, and said, "It was getting dark, so we had to leave the mountain. We decided to bring the deer to the emergency clinic, because we were afraid it would die."

"I would have made the same choice," I told them. "If you'll look closely, you can see that flies have laid eggs in his hair. That's a sure sign the mother was no longer with her baby."

As I examined the little creature, I let them know that there was no guarantee that the fawn could be saved, but I reassured them that we'd do all we could.

It was late Saturday night, and we discovered, to our dismay, that there were no bottles in the clinic supply room suitable for a tiny deer. Most stores had closed hours earlier.

"I'll have to go buy a baby bottle," I told the vet tech.

At the nearest all-night convenience store, I left the truck motor running and hurried to the doorway. I popped my head in and hollered at the cashier, who was talking on the phone, "You got any baby bottles?"

She looked up, astonished, clamping her palm over the mouthpiece of the phone.

"Say what?"

"You got any baby bottles?"

Her eyes said she was afraid I was a nut. Then she barked, "No, we ain't got no baby bottles." She began talking into the phone again, but kept her eyes on me as I hopped back in the truck. I could imagine her telling the person on the other end of the line about the man who acted like he was desperate for baby bottles, and saying, "He ought to have thought of that a long time ago."

I got much the same response at the next three stores I tried, but hit pay dirt at the fifth place. The cashier rummaged around at the back of a shelf, and found a plastic-wrapped pack containing a bottle with a cartoon character printed on it. She blew the dust off.

"Thanks a lot," I said and shoved three dollar bills in her hand. "Keep the change."

She told me I still owed her another 49 cents, plus tax. We settled the bill, and I broke a few traffic laws getting back to the clinic. I feared that my search might have taken more time than the fawn had to spare. Though I hadn't been gone all that long, I had broken a rule by leaving the clinic, and I was hoping no emergencies had come up in my unlawful absence.

Bottle in hand, I raced inside the clinic, ready for bad news. But the fawn was still alive. The vet tech had cleaned him up, removed the maggots and wrapped him warmly. He was so weak, we had to coax him to suck and swallow formula from the baby bottle, which he didn't want to take at first. His stomach had shrivelled since his last feeding of mother's milk, so we fed him often.

A couple of days later, we were relieved to see him growing stronger and more eager to take the bottle. The fawn flourished under the tender, loving care the clinic staff lavished on him.

Someone named him Little Bucky. We carried him in our arms when we weren't busy with other patients. He gave little grunts whenever he was looking for someone to cuddle him. We figured that was the way he would have communicated with his mother if he were with her in the woods. Once he was cradled in someone's arms, he hushed. His favorite trick was to suck the ear lobe of the person carrying him. We were his family.

One of the clinic technicians drove a covered camper. We got a kick out of tooling around town with Little Bucky and the vet tech's Rottweiler and Norwegian Elkhound peering out the back windows.

Sometimes, we went swimming at a nearby state park. Little Bucky loved it. He couldn't stand to be left behind on the bank. But we had to watch our backs, because he would try to climb on us when we were swimming. When we sprawled on our towels to catch some sun, Little Bucky walked all over us, jabbing us with his sharp hooves as he made himself a nest on the bath towels. He would snuggle close to the dogs and go to sleep.

Once, as the animals snoozed following a swim, a man and a little boy strolled by. The man noticed Little Bucky curled up with the two dogs.

"Son, what do you think about that dog?" he teased.

The child, who was about three or four, stared at the sleeping animals and turned to his father with an exasperated look. "Daddy! That looks a lot like a deer," the little boy said, his voice convicting his father of being really stupid.

Of course, the time came when Little Bucky was not so little any more. He had outgrown the clinic, and our care. We began to prepare him for survival in the wild. The adjustment was hard on us, too, but we reduced the amount of time we spent with him and took other steps to acclimate him to an independent life.

We searched for just the right place for Little Bucky's transition. We found it outside Biltmore Forest, near Asheville, North Carolina. A friend of one of the clinic employees lived on a back-country road. Her orchard and thickly forested property would offer Little Bucky a safe haven. No hunting was allowed in the area.

The lady, who lived alone in a house set back by itself in the woods, promised to keep an eye out for our beloved pet. She was an independent mountain woman with a love of animals. When we let him out in her orchard, Little Bucky inspected his surroundings, then bounded off into the woods with graceful leaps. He didn't even notice when we left.

We kept in touch with Little Bucky's new friend from time to time by telephone. It was good news when she reported that she had seen him traveling with an old buck. It appeared that Bucky had made a successful transition and become a creature of the wild. Gradually, the months passed, and the interval between calls from Biltmore Forest lengthened.

Later that year, the morning after the first frost of winter, Little Bucky's friend telephoned and said she had a story to tell.

"I was asleep last night," she said, "when all of a sudden I felt a draft. I thought I had left the door open. Before I could move, this hairy creature nibbled my earlobe. I was too scared to move, but then it started sucking on my ear, and I remembered Little Bucky."

Little Bucky was up to his old tricks.

"I didn't know what in the world to do!" she laughed.

"Well," I suggested, "when anything that big and fuzzy kisses you in the middle of the night, you'd better kiss him back."

She cackled as she finished her story.

"I turned the light on, went in the kitchen, found an old apple, and enticed Bucky out the back door," she said. "By the way, you don't need to call him Little Bucky any more. The name don't fit worth a toot. He's a mighty big feller now."

Before she hung up, though, I advised her to start locking her doors.

"Not everybody's as sweet and lovable as Little Bucky," I warned.

Several years later, after I began practicing in Easley, I somehow ended up trying to find another deer a suitable home when a wildlife officer brought in a large young doe for treatment.

The doe had been bruised and badly cut when she got tangled in a fence at a construction site on the Clemson University campus. The university is located next to Lake Hartwell, where deer and other wild animals roam freely, sometimes to the animals' detriment. Officers from the S.C. Marine and Wildlife Commission or state forest rangers frequently bring us injured birds or animals to treat.

The doe had severe lacerations from her battle with the sharp edges of a broken chain link fence and had suffered a great deal of stress before she was captured. I sutured her cuts, administered antibiotics and put her in our pen for a couple of weeks until she healed.

I had told my father about the deer. He suggested that I bring her to his place. Daddy has some acreage in Oconee County, and I thought it would be the ideal place to set her free.

"Bring her anytime," he said.

I decided to accept his offer on my next day off. My plan, which I thought was pretty good, was to give her a shot of anesthesia to keep her sleeping peacefully in the bed of my truck while we made that 45-minute ride to her new home. I knew I could cut a few minutes off the trip if I hit all four traffic lights in downtown Pickens, the county seat, just right. I gave the injection and waited. The minute she was out, we lifted her into the bed of the truck and off I went. I put an extra syringe of Rompum in the cab, just in case.

As I turned onto Main Street in Pickens, which is also the highway to Walhalla, I saw people congregated around the beautiful Williamsburg-style courthouse, and I realized that it was court week. *Rats.* I got caught by the first red light. As I waited for the traffic light to turn green, I studied the faces of people milling about, wondering which were the criminals and their lawyers, and which were the victims of crime.

The truck shuddered; I thought the motor was running rougher than usual and made a note to myself to adjust the timing when I got to Daddy's. Then I realized the folks on the courthouse lawn were looking my way. Grinning. I smiled back uneasily. I glanced in the rear view mirror casually, acting cool, curious to see what was going on behind me that was so amusing.

I froze. The deer was trying to stand in the bed of the truck. The anesthesia was wearing off. She had been out for only 15 minutes and should have stayed down another half hour.

I shoved the gearshift into park and grabbed the extra syringe. I thanked God I had brought it. All we needed was a loose deer crashing into the courtroom or through one of the store windows. I hurled myself into the bed of the truck with the deer.

She became more alert and began throwing her 100 pounds around, intent on getting out. I flopped my 190 pounds on top of her, hoping to hold her still, determined to give her another shot. I got a headlock and wrestled her to her knees. The doe and I bounced around for what seemed like hours.

Every time my head popped up over the rim, I caught a glimpse of the courthouse crowd watching us with delight. Clerks and customers came out of stores and stood near the truck, laughing and making jokes about my predicament.

I tried to ignore the spectators, but I could feel my face turning red as I held on for dear life to the squirming doe. Finally, the shot took effect. The doe was quiet.

Applause broke out as I climbed in the cab with my hand on the brim of my baseball cap. The crowd probably thought I was tipping my hat. Actually I was trying to shield my identity, as embarrassed as if I had been caught in a criminal act.

The rest of the trip was fast, but uneventful. Daddy and I watched the deer come to her senses. She strolled into the woods as if she knew she had found a home.

Daddy threw back his head and howled when I told him what had happened. It took a while before I saw the humor of the situation; then I admitted to myself that it was not the first time an animal had made a fool of me, and it probably wouldn't be the last.

Anyway, as I told Daddy, maybe I actually performed a real community service. Most of the folks who watched me make a fool of myself were waiting their turn before the judge. I may have given them the only laugh they had all day.

Chapter 31

"Please Don't Shoot Him!"

Late one evening, after the clinic had closed, my partner Jim and I were discussing business matters. It had been a busy day. By the time we had gotten through, we were too beat to start right away for home. We sat idly batting the breeze in the office we shared with our other partner. It was relaxing to sit in the rare quiet of our clinic while everything was sleeping.

Jim kind of chuckled to himself and asked, "Did I ever tell you about the time when Poag went to Virginia to get a bull for his dad?" I propped my feet on my desk and leaned back in my rump-sprung chair. I was ready to listen to a tale.

Poag Reid was Jim's college roommate and long-time friend who has a large animal practice in a nearby town. This is the story Jim told:

Poag had just got his driver's license; you can get one in South Carolina when you turn fifteen. He had been driving tractors and trucks on his family's farm outside Rock Hill since he was a little kid, and over the years he had earned his dad's trust.

Mr. Reid told Poag to drive the big cattle hauler up to Virginia to collect a Charolais bull he had agreed to buy. This would be the first Charolais bull in their county. He put $2,000 in Poag's hand to pay for the bull, and some more for gas and meals on the trip. The breeder's farm was just above the North Carolina line.

Poag's pride swelled near to bursting over this responsibility. He felt like a man. The next morning, before it was light, he and his buddy, Brad, set out in the cattle truck. But they had barely gotten out of sight of home when the truck overheated. Poag coasted to the grassy shoulder of the two-lane highway and parked the truck.

Brad worried that the trip was off. Not Poag. His father had trusted him to bring a bull home, and that's what he was going to do.

"We'll go back and get the other truck," Poag said. He and Brad struck out walking back to the farm. Both of his parents had left for work. Poag got the keys to the battered, 1951 half-ton Chevy pickup the Reids used to haul hay, seed and feed. The sun was barely peeping above the horizon when they set out again for the breeding farm, some four or five hours away.

They enjoyed looking at the magnificent cattle grazing in lush pastures as they drove along through North Carolina and into Virginia. Shortly after they grabbed a quick lunch, they arrived at the Charolais farm. They parked the pickup and walked up the steps to the wraparound front porch of the sprawling house.

Poag introduced himself and Brad to the man who responded to Poag's knock, and explained that his dad had sent them to collect his new bull. With a sense of importance, he carefully counted the bull's purchase price from the roll of money that burdened his pocket.

The cattleman took the bills, wrote a receipt and handed over the papers on his blooded bull—offspring of champions on both sides. Then he looked around, puzzled.

"What you going to haul him in, son?" the Virginian asked, looking for their cattle truck.

Poag pointed at his pickup. "There's the truck."

"You plan to carry that bull to South Carolina in a pickup?" the breeder asked, disbelieving.

Poag, determined to prove he was man enough to handle the situation, nodded and lied confidently, "Yessir! We haul our cattle around in it all the time."

The cattleman didn't argue. He figured it wasn't any of his business if Poag's dad sent his kid off to haul a purebred Charolais bull home in a pickup; but Poag and Brad could tell the man had his doubts. Their fifteen-year-old pride left no room for thoughts of failure.

Nonetheless, the farmer helped them load the bull onto the truck. When the huge animal was on board, the dented, rusted bed of the Chevy sank down almost onto the tires. The back end was lower than the front, and the hood thrust skyward.

Poag looked at the bull in the small truck and thought—to himself of course—that it was possible the bull might come out over the top. So Poag rigged a make-shift halter from a big rope he found in the truck's messy floorboard. He snugged the halter tight, then ran the lead rope back behind the cab and down through a hole in the bed. He pulled the slack out and secured the rope around the half-ton's frame.

The cattleman checked the tie ropes one last time. As Poag drove out of the barnyard, exercising extra caution, the bull's breeder walked alongside the truck a little way, talking through the open window. "You be real careful, boys. You sure, now, you'll be okay?" he asked, as if he was having second thoughts. "You sho' wouldn't want anything to happen to that bull."

The massive weight in the truck bed raised the front end, and steering was difficult. Their pace toward home was a lot slower than it had been earlier in the morning.

Little did the teenagers realize what an amazing sight they and their bull were. The bull's massive head jutted over the cab; he looked as if he were resting his chin on the thin roof. His muscular body stretched the length of the bed of the pickup so that his tail hung over the tailgate. The boys tooled along, oblivious to the startled looks they drew from occupants in passing vehicles.

The sun was getting low; their shadow ran along the ground beside them in the fading light as they hit the outskirts of Charlotte. Brad told Poag that he knew a short cut through town that would save them some time. The route he directed took them through a residential area. They could see people sitting on porches or loitering on the crumbly, littered sidewalks turning to look at the huge cargo in the ratty old truck. Other drivers stared.

"We're like a parade!" Brad hooted. "Look at everybody watching us!"

They stopped as a traffic light turned red. The bull was tired after standing in the same spot for several hours, wind and bugs whiffling against his face. He stamped his feet fretfully, and the truck swayed.

"I'll be glad when we get home. An hour ought to do it," Poag said. He checked the side mirror to get a better view of his precious freight.

Suddenly, the truck lurched wildly, followed by a foghorn blast that issued from the dark recesses of the bull's chest, then a hiss. The stink of burning hair spewed in the windows. Poag cut the engine. He and Brad sprang out into the street and ran around to look at the bull. Their faces paled: one of the bull's hind legs had punched a hole through a half-rotted plank and was trapped against the hot exhaust pipe.

As soon as Poag saw the bull's predicament, he sprang into action. His top priority was to get the bull's leg away from the pipe. He shouted to Brad to open the tailgate as he jumped into the bed of the truck with the bull. Poag yanked out his pocket knife and slashed the rope attached to the bull's halter. The bed of the truck bounced and bucked as the bull tried to stomp the truck into the pavement.

Free of the restraining rope, the bull pulled his hoof free. With a great leap, the bull hurled himself out of the pickup, pieces of rope dangling from each side of his leather halter. The Charolais landed on the pavement with a great thud, scrambled to get his balance, then thundered off into the not-so-wide-open spaces of downtown Charlotte.

Howling bystanders scattered. Mamas and grandmammas snagged little children from the cluttered yards and raced through doorways of the houses, the babies screaming with the sudden shock of being carted from play like sacks of potatoes.

Poag and Brad raced frantically after the bull. It dodged cars, bikes, tricycles and trampled through

199

flower beds, hedges and postage-stamp–sized gardens. Poag and his pal stayed hot on the bull's heels. As he ran, Poag tried to piece together the rope he had cut, his fingers fumbling as he attempted to make a lasso.

People left their cars in the street to join the chase. The posse streamed behind the two teenagers, their whooping and hollering adding to the bull's panic. The pursuers shouted contradictory instructions to one another.

Poag heard a siren blaring its way toward them and caught sight of flashing lights against the growing dusk. A police car screeched to a halt in the middle of the street where spectators had gathered. Just as Poag shot out from behind a house, he saw the policeman step out of the patrol car. The huge Charolais galloped across the street directly in front of the vehicle. The cop reacted instinctively. He bent his knees and ran, stooping low, toward the panicking animal, pulling his gun from the holster on his hip.

"Don't shoot him!" Poag screamed at the top of his lungs. "Don't shoot him!"

The cop froze, looking around, and saw a terrified teenager rushing toward him.

"I got to shoot him," the young cop hollered back.

"Please, sir! Please don't shoot him! That's my daddy's bull! I gotta get him home! My dad will kill me if you shoot that bull!" Poag was near tears. The policeman, a rookie only a few years older than Poag, looked around, realized the bull had disappeared anyway, and put his gun back in the holster.

Just then, a hullabaloo went up behind a nearby house. Poag and the policeman ran in tandem toward the screamers. Poag was in the lead and hot on the bull's trail as it fled behind a house.

It was time for Poag's luck to turn, and it did. He swung the rope around the bull's neck as it swiveled around, uncertain how to get out of the trap of a fenced yard. Poag flipped the other end of the rope around the metal frame of a child's swing set, and figured that he had the bull under control.

Not so. The bull strained against the restraining rope; its weight and momentum pulled the swing set's metal frame and its cement footings from the ground. The bull set off in search of freedom.

The bull-chasers and spectators scattered in all directions, spilling on top of each other, shouting fearfully. The policeman pulled his gun again, aiming at the bellowing bull as it lumbered down the sidewalk with the swing set clanking and tossing sparks. Poag grabbed the policeman's arm. "Please! I beg you! Don't shoot my daddy's bull!"

Car horns began a bleeping, hellish cacophony at the intersection, where traffic had come to a sudden halt—hoods, fenders and bumpers perilously close to total chaos. The swing's frame had wedged against a fire hydrant. The animal twisted around in such a fashion that his head was firmly pinioned against the hydrant. He struggled and snorted, but to no avail. The bull had finally, literally, come to the end of its rope.

Poag and Brad kept pace with the policeman as they came close to the panting, trapped animal.

"Mister, just help me get some planks for the truck and some rope, and we'll get that bull back on the truck and leave," Poag promised. "We don't have far to go."

Poag's earnest plea struck a sympathetic chord with the policeman. Once again, he holstered his pistol. Then the cop glanced around and asked the crowd if anyone knew where they could get a few planks and some rope.

As if of one mind, the people of the neighborhood rallied. Someone found a sheet of plywood that exactly fit the busted bed of the truck. Others brought bits of lumber, hammers, and strands of rope. Their efforts bound together by chords of laughter, the volunteers restored the truck to service, the bull to the truck, and the neighborhood to a jolly, high-spirited peace.

Poag looked sadly at the exhausted Charolais' leg. It had a nasty burn. But the bull was alive! The weary bull laid his head on the cab of the truck and blinked his eyes in the unfamiliar glow of city lights.

Poag and Brad shook hands with the cop, touched the nearest hands of those who had helped through the crisis, and got back in the pickup.

Once again, the Chevy's hood tilted and its tail dragged. Poag and his friend waved at the crowd. Many waved back; most looked at each other and grinned. For half an hour, it had been marvelous mayhem, a change in the dull routine of a summer evening.

A police car followed the truck to the city limits, blinked its lights, then did a U-turn, heading back into the busy city.

An everlastingly long hour later, Poag and Brad wheeled into the darkened farm, silent with fatigue. Despite their troubles, Poag was glad that he had not totally let his dad down. The bull was home.

Still, he was afraid to let his dad see the bull in its injured condition. The teenagers unloaded the

Charolais into a back pasture and stood watching the creamy white hide of the bull fade to gray as he wandered away toward a small branch trickling under a grove of trees. The cows resting nearby would keep the bull company.

Brad went home. Poag decided not to awaken his parents. He went to bed. Things surely would be better and a lot easier to explain in the clear light of day.

Poag awakened, dressed slowly—full of dread—and went to the kitchen. His father was eating breakfast. His mother sipped coffee. A curtain of silence seemed to hang over the table.

Finally, Mr. Reid looked up from his paper and said, "Poag, did you get the bull yesterday?"

"Yessir," Poag answered, hoping that the fact that the new bull was home would be enough information to satisfy his father's curiosity.

"How did it get here? I saw the truck sitting on the side of the highway," Mr. Reid said.

Poag had never lied to his dad and wasn't about to start now.

"I hauled him back in the Chevy pickup," he replied.

"You did what...?"

The whole incredible story poured out in a torrent, and to Poag's great surprise, his father listened calmly, if bemusedly—at the end saying only that they should go and check on the bull. After inspecting the bull's burned leg, both understood that, like youthful foibles, it would heal with time.

Chapter 32

Python Passion

It got to be our daily greeting: "Where's the python this morning?"

For nearly a week, our clinic's staff started the work day with a search for one of our patients—an elusive python that was an escape artist. The person who opened the clinic initiated the search, and those who came in later raised the question of the day. If the python had not been found, the whole staff had a job cut out for them.

The python was six feet long, and the much-loved pet and companion of a man who was a paraplegic. He had brought the snake in for treatment of a myocotic infection. The python had to have daily baths in medicated water to heal the skin disease. His owner, confined to a wheelchair, was not able to give his pet the daily dips, so the snake became a patient in our animal hospital.

The python was a friendly creature, but he was a Houdini. Despite all our efforts to keep him safely sealed in a large plastic tub at night, nothing worked. We weighed down a screen on top of the tub, but every morning, the screen was tipped back just enough for the python to slither out and cause our morning panic.

We were afraid he would disappear down a drain or through some hidey-hole in the building. We locked him in the surgery room where there were no drains that he could get into, but he still found places to hide.

His loss, we knew, would cause his owner a great deal of grief, so it was always a relief when someone called out, "I've found him!" We would haul the six-foot-long snake from under a table, or out of a drawer, or from some dark corner. We cleared out a lot of dust looking for that reptile.

The python's owner called every day to check on the progress of his pet. He sounded worried, but he was heartened to learn his snake was responding to the antibiotics and baths we gave him. It was obvious the man was lonely without his python. The guy had lost the use of his legs in an accident and spent most of his days working in an office in his home. The python was his constant companion.

The morning that I told him his snake was ready to go home, the man's voice regained its vigor. He promised he would be at the clinic within a hour.

He was as good as his word. In a short while, he arrived in his van and maneuvered his wheelchair into the lobby.

I got the python out of his cage and headed toward the front desk with it in my arms. As we approached the lobby, I could hear the snake's owner talking to the receptionist. The snake's body grew stiff with tension. Its head turned from side to side; the forked tongue flickered so quickly, it was almost invisible. The snake was trembling in my arms.

The man in the wheelchair was almost hidden by the desk as I came through the door with the python, but he saw us, and called out, "Hey, Buddy!"

The snake nearly went wild. I had to keep a tight hold to prevent it from slithering out of my arms. Most of the snake's body was stretched rigid, parallel to the floor, its eyes focused on the man who continued talking to it with tender words of welcome.

The snake surged into its owner's open arms. I swear, if it had been a dog, it would have barked and given its owner a sloppy lick. The python curled around the man's broad shoulders, and I could see it relax as the man stroked the now soft, sleek skin.

I told the man about the snake's nightly escapes.

"We'd begun to think he was trying to run away and find his way home," I joked.

As I watched them enjoying their reunion, I felt that there was something going on that text books didn't tell us about snakes. If that python didn't feel love for the man who cradled him, it was the next closest thing.

We would have found a permanent home for another reptile—a stowaway from Brazil—but the officers of the law intervened and hauled him away.

A trucker for an asphalt company brought us a sick, tick-covered and nearly-starved iguana from Brazil. The creature had traveled undetected across the seas, and then across South Carolina, before it was discovered in one of the trucks.

The truck driver said he saw the lizard crawl out of an asphalt truck; the vehicle had been used on a project in Brazil and then was shipped back to South Carolina. It had been driven from the port in Charleston to

Mauldin. When the truck was parked, the long-distance traveler crawled out.

The iguana was suffering the effects of many days of confinement with no food or water, no exercise, and temperature changes that would tax the strength of almost any living thing. The ticks that infested its scaly skin were weird; their coloration almost exactly matched the lizard's.

We removed the ticks, administered medicine and gave the iguana a nourishing, vegetarian diet. We kept him in isolation, since he was an imported creature. The iguana's long days as a captive on board the truck had left him with a yearning for companionship, and with daily handling as we treated him, he calmed rapidly.

We named the creature Iggy, and found his prehistoric ugliness endearing.

Iggy was hale and hearty again when I remembered that all animals coming into the country had to go through quarantine. Iggy was an illegal alien and had violated immigration laws. I figured we'd better be law-abiding citizens, so I called the state laboratory and explained how the iguana had come into our care.

"We had two priorities," I told the official. "One was to take care of the iguana's medical needs. The second was to protect the poultry industry," I said, trying to explain the delay in calling the agency. "We've kept the iguana in isolation."

I reassured the official of how careful we had been to keep Iggy out of contact with other animals, since he might have had some contagious disease. Certain diseases he might carry could devastate the poultry industry, so we had been careful with Iggy's care.

Responding more quickly than one usually expects from the government, two officious gentlemen showed up at our clinic and demanded the iguana. We handed Iggy over to the gray suits. They hardly looked at the little creature who had waddled his way into our hearts.

"We can get Iggy back after he goes through quarantine, can't we?" I asked.

The officers looked at each other, then one shrugged his shoulders as the other said in a pompous voice: "I really can't say, sir."

The truth was, we were saying goodbye. Where the red tape led Iggy, we were never privileged to know.

Chapter 33

To Bee or Not to Bee

It was a boiling day in July when my dad decided, in the heat of the afternoon, that an urgent job had to be done. His beehive needed repairs. The brood chamber had rotted and needed to be replaced.

Although I didn't see why this job couldn't hold until a cooler moment, I had a few hours to spare, so I went out to give him a hand. We put the new chamber and combs in his old truck, along with his veiled hat and smoker, and I drove him out to the edge of the pasture where he had set up his hive near a stand of field pines.

We drove along, enjoying our view of the mountains. I slowed down as we passed clumps of cows, so I could check the state of their health, then we cut out across the pasture.

Some of the cows began traipsing along behind the familiar truck, their great udders sloshing left and right rhythmically as they hurried along. Cows have a lot of curiosity, and Daddy's cows wanted to know what he was doing. They thought he might have a bale of hay for them. Others spotted the string of spectators in our wake and headed in our direction. Before long, we had a convoy of cows going to watch Daddy fix the beehive.

The weathered bee gum sat on a terrace braced by a wall of rocks. Branches of gnarly pines drooped over the hive. Bees soared around like planes at a busy airport as they deposited nectar in the hive, then departed to continue their collection.

I backed the truck so the tailgate was nearly level with the terrace. That would make it easier for Daddy to work, with his equipment close at hand. Daddy put on his "uniform" before he approached the hive. His broad-brimmed hat was topped by a veil which draped around the shoulders of his long-sleeved shirt. The veil had a drawstring in the hem that he tightened to keep the bees from his neck and face. As he drew the bottom of the veil tight, I noticed that the string was about four or five feet long. He tucked the excess string inside his belt. Why there was such an excess, I never knew.

The only other equipment he carried was the smoke can. It contained pieces of old jeans which he set afire. The cotton fibers burned slowly inside the metal can, and white smoke puffed from the spout. He waved the smoke can around the hive. The smoke would make the bees lethargic enough to allow him to transfer them and their queen to the new hive peaceably.

I stayed inside the truck. Bees are Billy Orr's project, not mine. No matter how sweet and tasty honey is, I never figured it was worth the pain of bee stings. I daydreamed as I watched the cows milling around, some standing quietly eyeing Daddy's work, others more interested in snagging grass once they realized that we had no treats for them.

In the rear view mirror, I could see Daddy leaning over the old hive. But as he picked it up, it collapsed under its own weight. As he struggled to hold on, his veil caught on a branch and gapped open. The bees poured in on his face.

The mass of hive and bees dropped from Daddy's hands. Angry bees exploded everywhere. Suddenly, the cows closest to us stampeded across the pasture, as sounds like BB-gun pellets thunked against the truck windows and the cab roof. Bees dive-bombed the truck, swarming madly. I swivelled my head left and right, trying to check on Daddy.

He was gone! He was nowhere in sight! Then I spotted a hat in the middle of the fleeing herd, and could see the veil trailing like angel wings as Daddy galloped away from the enraged bees. I was impressed. I didn't know my dad had that kind of speed. Finally, he maneuvered his way out of the middle of the fleeing cows, and headed straight for the truck. Bees buzzed around his head, and I could tell from the way his hands swatted his neck and face that he was being stung by intruders under the veil.

All of a sudden, as he leapt across a terrace, his foot caught in an old strand of barbed wire. It jerked him horizontal in mid-air. He flew headfirst into the truck door. Bees blanketed him. He stood up, reaching for the door handle.

I leaned over and locked the door. I hated to do it, but hey, he had a veil and I didn't. He grabbed the door handle, yelling: "Let me in! Let me in!" I shook my head no. He looked astonished and furious when he realized that the door was locked, and he couldn't get into the cab with me.

I had seen that expression on his face before. It meant, "I'll kill you when I catch you!"

I shook my head again and frantically motioned my hand to signal him to get in the back of the truck. He finally got the idea, and fell headlong into the truck bed. I dumped the clutch and stomped on the gas. In the rear view mirror, I could see Daddy wallowing from one side of the truck to the other as we fish-tailed away from the terrace.

When I thought we were a safe distance away from most of the swarm, I slammed on the brakes, jumped out and helped Daddy beat the bees off. He was as mad as a swarm of bees himself. I could see welts popping up where bees had zapped him.

"You want to get in now and go home?" I asked.

"No!"

Grim-faced, Daddy settled his veil about his shoulders and hopped on the tailgate. One thing about my daddy—he's stubborn. He wholeheartedly believes that old saying, "If at first you don't succeed, try, try again." I backed the truck against the terrace so he could try again.

Daddy got the new hive in place and was reaching down to get the new combs. He ducked beneath one of the over-hanging branches. The tip caught his veil and tipped his hat to one side, exposing his neck, now wet with sweat. The odor of his perspiration must have set the bees off, because they got riled all over again.

Daddy didn't even hesitate. He jumped into the truck bed, banged his fist on the cab, grabbed hold on one side, and off we went again with a great leap. That ought to have been enough for most folks, but not Daddy. We waited 'til the bees calmed down; then back we went to the terrace. He smoked the hive good, and the bees were transformed into passive little house-holders, snugly settling into their new quarters.

Daddy had kept control of his temper, but he was still angry, and he took it out on the old hive. Rather than haul it back to the barn to add to the plunder there, he decided to hurl it out into the briars, near the edge of the woods.

He picked the old hive up and gave a great fling, unaware that the long string of his veiled hat had worked free of his belt and was dangling around his knees. The string snagged on a rusted nail as the hive went sailing through the air. Daddy's body lurched for-ward with a jerk as the hive arced to the ground and shattered. Dust and wood chips flew everywhere.

I was busting a gut laughing, but I stopped when he picked himself off the ground and got back in the truck, slamming the door as he plopped into the seat. He fumed silently, too exasperated for words. I didn't say a word either. There wasn't much I could have said anyway, and to have laughed in his presence would have been unkind, not to mention risky.

In a little while, Daddy focused his frustration on the fact that I had locked the door.

"I just can't believe I raised such a son," he kept repeating as we bounced over the pasture, back toward the barn.

I didn't laugh anymore until I was well out of his sight, sharing the story with my brothers, Wayne, Jim and Mickey.

Chapter 34

Angel in the Arbor

I've got to tell you just one more bull story before we get to the end. I want to tell it, because it's about a kind of miracle.

Andy Taylor is an agriculture teacher, and he lives out on the west side of the county toward the lakes. He's got a real nice young family. Their place is about the prettiest little farm you would ever want to see, set right up close at the foot of a mountain.

Andy called me one day and said his big old Simmental bull was limping. Said he couldn't see what the problem was. "Come on out, quick as you can," he said. "I've got him penned up, and he don't like it one little bit."

Only half of that was true by the time I got there.

I jumped in the truck and went charging out there. It was summer, green and just a beautiful day. I drove through the gate and up the driveway, where the yard just sort of blossoms out into the house area. I went past the picturesque little house and back to the barn.

The barn is built on the hillside so that the stalls are underneath and the loft is level with the driveway. You can just drive right into the loft and unload hay.

So I drive up to the loft and stop. There is a terrible commotion going on down below. I get out and walk over where I can look down. That bull has already got loose. Andy has some chickens penned down there, and the bull is butting the pen. He butts, and the chickens squawk and flutter and holler, and he butts again. The feathers are just a-flying.

I look down there, thinking, *Oh, law, that's what I've got to work on—that thing that's creating all that havoc.* While I look at him, the bull walks up to a pair of closed double doors, and just walks right through, taking the hinges and all.

I run out to the truck and get a syringe full of anesthetic, thinking it will calm him down a little bit. Now he is pawing around in the lot. There are posts lying in there where Andy has been building a squeeze chute. He hasn't finished the head gate, but I figure I can run the bull into the chute and throw posts in behind him to hold him.

The bull goes into the chute, and I fling posts in behind him. Now, when he can't back out, he just puts his head under the rails and lifts up. He just lifts the posts right out of the ground, and the fence falls over his neck like a yoke.

That annoys him. Suddenly, that joker takes a step backwards, and then he jumps. He does a high-jump right onto that jumble of poles, and I jump up behind him. While he is teeter-tottering up there, I catch him by the rump and give him the shot; he flops backwards into the chute, facing now the way he wants to go.

215

He runs and jumps over the first gate, and then the second one, crashes through the fence, and he's out on the lawn, making for the road. And I am running after him, thinking, *Lawsuit! Automobile wreck!*

But he gets sidetracked. Andy has this beautiful grape arbor—two rows of posts with beautiful, thick vines growing on them.

The medicine is beginning to work; the bull is losing his edge. He begins bumping down that arbor. One post after another, bump...bump...the posts go down, he's tossing his head, throwing the vines around with his horns. He takes one whole row. The vines sag down. Then he sees the kids' sandbox, and he walks up there and stomps the sandbox, crunches all the little buckets and dump trucks, then he comes back to take the other side of the trellis. Bump...bump....

He's getting wobbly and bored. He turns around, takes a run for the fence, and jumps back into the pasture. He's so drunk now, I can get him with the lariat. I rope him, and he goes right down. In the soft part of his hoof, there's a plain old roofing nail. Terribly painful. I pull it out and clean out the abscess. He'll sleep it off. He'll feel a lot better than Andy will when Andy sees all this destruction.

When I head up to the house, I pass that mess of grapevines. There is motion among the leaves. Andy's little five-year-old sits up and peeks out of what had been the arbor. She was in there that whole time, hiding from the bull. She and her guardian angel.

She has been peeping out, watching the whole thing. "Mister," she says, "you ought to be on 'That's Incredible.' "

And, I think, *Little Girl, so should you.*

216

Chapter 35

Kissing My Turtle Goodbye

Any time you think you've heard it all, the phone rings and proves you wrong.

This time, it was a female voice. A nurse. "Doctor Orr?" she said, "This is the emergency room at Easley Baptist. We have a little boy coming in with a snapping turtle on his lip. Can you give us any ideas about how to handle this situation?"

I sat stunned for a second. "A snapping turtle has bit a little boy's lip?" I asked. I shivered.

"Yes, sir," the nurse said. "His mother just called. They're on their way to the hospital right now. None of us has ever had a situation like this, and one of the nurses suggested we call you."

I thought of my little boy, Ethan; it was too awful to imagine the pain of little-boy lips with a big old turtle hanging on. Biting. Its beady eyes staring without remorse. I knew that little kid was suffering, and his parents must be scared out of their wits.

"What should we do?" the nurse wanted to know. "If it won't turn loose, should we cut off the turtle's head? If that's what we have to do, how do we do it?"

"Oh, Lord, no!" I hollered. "Whatever you do, don't kill that turtle!" I could see too well what could happen then. That kid could be wearing a turtle head on his mouth when he went away to college. He would be the only kid in history who couldn't get a girl friend because his turtle lip repelled romance.

Trying to stay calm, I said to her, "If you cut off its head, its muscles will reflex and cause more trauma. It will just clamp down and *stay*. Or it could take a huge chunk out of the boy's mouth. Tell the staff that!"

I heard her relay my message to others in the ER. I was thinking desperately about alternative solutions as she talked to someone in the background. Then she came back to me.

"What are we going to do, then?"

"What I hope is that it hasn't really bitten through his lip yet. It may be just hanging on," I said. I told her, "Try to force your largest hemostats between the turtle's jaws, so it can't clamp down. Push hemostats in on both sides of the jaws, and then try to pry its mouth open." The metal clamps would protect the child's lip— I hoped—by keeping the snapping turtle's powerful jaws from locking more tightly on the tender flesh.

The nurse murmured, "Yes, okay, yes," as I talked. Then she interrupted, "Wait a minute, please. They're coming in." The receiver clunked as she laid it down. I could hear muffled sounds of hustling, and excited voices in the background. Then a voice carried clearly into the phone: "They're coming. They're here. Oh, God...the thing is as big as a dinner plate!"

The nurse came back on the line. "The little boy is here," she said, "and Doctor Orr, the turtle is huge. It has the boy's lower lip in its...beak? I told the doctor what you said to do, and that's what we're getting ready to do now...."

"How old is the child?" I asked her.

"He's about seven, bless his heart. That turtle looks vicious. Oh, I can hardly stand to see it," she said. "Look, I've got to go. Thanks for the help, Doctor Orr."

"How about calling me back as soon as you can?" I asked. "So I'll know how things go, okay?"

"Sure thing," she said.

For the next five or ten minutes, I stewed and worried and hurt for that little boy. What was happening at the hospital? For a minute or two, I thought about dropping everything and driving over to the ER, which was only a few miles away. But we had our own patients to take care of, so I worked and listened for the phone.

One question kept running through my mind: How in the world did a little kid get his face so close to the jaws of a snapping turtle?

After what seemed forever, the ER nurse called back.

"I've got good news," she said, her voice full of joy. "The hemostats worked. It was perfect. The little boy's lip was bruised, but the turtle didn't bite even a little chunk out of it. The child's only going to have a swollen lip and sore mouth for a while."

The turtle, she added, was in a bucket, waiting for a ride back to its stream.

"That's great!" I said. She thanked me again and started to hang up, but I had to get my question answered.

"Wait a minute!" I said. "How did that kid get so close to a snapping turtle?"

She burst into laughter, full of relief. "His mother told us he was playing in a creek near their house and found the turtle. He had no idea how dangerous it was and brought it home to show his mother.

"Without thinking, she told the little boy to take the turtle back to the creek, leave it there, and not to touch it again."

The nurse started laughing once more; I thought she had lost it when she blurted, "The kid kissed his turtle."

"He what?"

"That's what he said. He told us himself, after we got the turtle off his lip. His eyes filled with tears, and his voice was quivering. He said, 'I just wanted to kiss my turtle goodbye.' "